CONRAD'S
HEART OF DARKNESS
AND THE CRITICS

Wadsworth Guides to Literary Study

Maurice Beebe, General Editor

APPROACHES TO *WALDEN*
edited by Lauriat Lane, Jr., University of New Brunswick

CONRAD'S *HEART OF DARKNESS* AND THE CRITICS
edited by Bruce Harness, University of Illinois

CRIME AND PUNISHMENT AND THE CRITICS
edited by Edward Wasiolek, University of Chicago

DARWIN AND HIS CRITICS: The Darwinian Revolution
edited by Bernard R. Kogan, University of Illinois, Chicago

THE *KING LEAR* PERPLEX
edited by Helmut Bonheim, University of California, Santa Barbara

LITERARY CENSORSHIP: Principles, Cases, Problems
edited by Kingsley Widmer, San Diego State College, and Eleanor Widmer

LITERARY SYMBOLISM: An Introduction to the Interpretation of Literature
edited by Maurice Beebe, Purdue University

MELVILLE'S *BILLY BUDD* AND THE CRITICS
edited by William T. Stafford, Purdue University

THE RIME OF THE ANCIENT MARINER: A HANDBOOK
edited by Royal A. Gettmann, University of Illinois

A *SCARLET LETTER* HANDBOOK
edited by Seymour L. Gross, University of Notre Dame

CONRAD'S HEART OF DARKNESS AND THE CRITICS

EDITED BY BRUCE HARKNESS
University of Illinois

WADSWORTH PUBLISHING COMPANY, INC.
SAN FRANCISCO

First Printing, May 1960
Second Printing, January 1961
Third Printing, June 1961

L.C. Cat. Card No.: 60-9979

Printed in the United States of America.

Manufactured by American Book-Stratford Press, Inc.

CONTENTS

Preface ix
"Author's Note" to Youth *Volume* xiii

HEART OF DARKNESS 1

Conrad and the Congo

Joseph Conrad—The Congo Diary 71
G. Jean-Aubry—In the Heart of Darkness 81
Edward Garnett—On Conrad's Use of Memory 101

Interpreting the Story

Douglas Hewitt—Reassessment of "Heart of Darkness" 103
Albert J. Guerard—The Journey Within 111

The Duty of Marlow

M. C. Bradbrook—Marlow's Function 121
W. Y. Tindall—Apology for Marlow 123
Marvin Mudrick—Marlow and Conrad 134

Mythic and Literary Parallels: The Framework

Robert O. Evans—Conrad's Underworld 137
William Bysshe Stein—The Lotus Posture and "The Heart of Darkness" 145
Seymour L. Gross—A Further Note on the Function of the Frame in "Heart of Darkness" 148

The Lie

Walter F. Wright—Ingress to the Heart of Darkness 153
Thomas C. Moser—The Lie and Truth 156
Wilfred S. Dowden—The Light and Dark Lie 158

Textual Note 161
Study Questions, Theme and Paper Topics 169
Bibliography of Works for Further Study 175

To Leslie

PREFACE

This book is meant primarily for students in introductory literature classes, but it is hoped that other readers will find it interesting and valuable. The critical sections which follow "Heart of Darkness" represent most of the significant interpretations now held on the story, and should lead to a richer understanding of the tale which is generally considered Conrad's best. The student will readily discover that despite the intensity of critical commentary on Conrad—and since 1940 that commentary has increased immensely in quantity as well as quality—many problems of detail, interpretation, and evaluation are far from settled.

This book itself may, in a small way, help toward a solution of one important problem—that of Conrad's text. This is the first edition of "Heart of Darkness" based on a collation of all the important editions. The Textual Note supplied will permit the interested reader to trace sample variations through the basic publications of the story. More importantly, the note suggests that the reader need be somewhat wary of reprints of Conrad, and that a critical edition of his works is overdue.

The plan of this volume is a simple one. Following "Heart of Darkness," and commentaries on the biographical sources of the tale, are two critical essays to guide the over-all interpretation of the story. Then some of the basic issues of the story are discussed: the function of Marlow as narrator, the meaning of his Lie to Kurtz's fiancée, the allusive quality of the story and its framework. Critics of differing viewpoints are represented. The student will find his understanding and appreciation of "Heart of Darkness" deepened; he will be stirred to further analysis and reading of Conrad. All citation-references by these critics to "Heart of Darkness" and "The Congo Diary" have, for the reader's convenience, been regularized to match the present volume. I have, further, given new titles to many of the critical selections. At the end of the volume are sections containing material for further study—a bibliography of works on Conrad, the Textual Note, and questions and suggested theme topics.

For the convenience of the student, page references to the original source of critical articles are given in raised numerals. That procedure has not been followed for "Heart of Darkness," since this volume presents a new, eclectic text. Otherwise, all material has been reproduced as exactly as possible from the original. The amount of material omitted from any article here reprinted can be ascertained by checking the original pagination, as indicated in the brackets. Whenever a page of the text in its original form ended with a divided word, I have ignored the division and placed the page reference at the end of the complete word. Unspaced ellipses (...) are the original author's; spaced ellipses (. . .) are mine. (It should be noted that, like the difference between italic and roman type for quotation marks and commas, these are in part matters of purely formal style or design.) Occasionally footnotes have been dropped, and the remaining ones renumbered; when the original author used two sets of notes—as some at the foot of his page, others at the back of his book—they have been edited into one series.

In addition to my thanks to the authors and publishers of the materials which make up this volume, I would like to record my further gratitude. To Edward Ratcliffe and Frank Rodgers of the University of Illinois Library, who helped me with Inter-Library loans. To the University of Kentucky Library, especially, for lending the Sun-Dial edition of Conrad. To Yale University Library for supplying a microfilm of the manuscript of the story. To Daniel Dungan, Mary Alice Heagarty, Gordon Lindstrand, and Norman Mysliwiec, who helped me with some of the collating. Special thanks are due to M. D. Zabel, who taught me Conrad in courses at the University of Chicago.

University of Illinois *B. H.*

HEART OF DARKNESS

from the volume

YOUTH

A NARRATIVE

AND TWO OTHER STORIES

. . . But the Dwarf answered: "No; something human is dearer to me than the wealth of all the world."—GRIMM'S TALES

TO
MY WIFE

Joseph Conrad

"Author's Note" to *Youth* Volume*

The three stories in this volume lay no claim to unity of artistic purpose. The only bond between them is that of the time in which they were written. They belong to the period immediately following the publication of the *Nigger of the Narcissus,* and preceding the first conception of *Nostromo,* two books which, it seems to me, stand apart and by themselves in the body of my work. It is also the period during which I contributed to "Maga"; a period dominated by *Lord Jim* and associated in my grateful memory with the late Mr. William Blackwood's encouraging and helpful kindness.

Youth was not my first contribution to "Maga." It was the second. But that story marks the first appearance in the world of the man Marlow, with whom my relations have grown very intimate in the course of years. The origins of that gentleman (nobody as far as I know had ever hinted that he was anything but that)—his origins have been the subject of some literary speculation of, I am glad to say, a friendly nature.

One would think that I am the proper person to throw a light on the matter; but in truth I find that it isn't so easy. It is pleasant to remember that nobody had charged him with fraudulent purposes or looked down on him as a charlatan; but apart from that he was supposed to be all sorts of things: a clever screen, a mere device, a "personator," a familiar spirit, a whispering "dæmon." I myself have been suspected of a meditated plan for his capture.

That is not so. I made no plans. The man Marlow and I came together in the casual manner of those health-resort acquaintances which sometimes ripen into friendships. This one has ripened. For all his assertiveness in matters of opinion he is not an intrusive person. He haunts my hours of solitude, when, in silence, we lay our heads together in great comfort and harmony; but as we part at the end of a tale I am never sure that it may not be for the last time. Yet I don't think that either of us would care much to survive the other. In his case, at any rate, his occupation would be gone and he would suffer from that extinction, because I suspect him of some vanity. I don't mean vanity in the Solomonian sense. Of all my people he's the one that has never been a vexation to my spirit. A most discreet, understanding man....

Even before appearing in book-form *Youth* was very well received.

---

* Reprinted from *Youth, A Narrative and Two Other Stories* with permission of the Trustees of the Joseph Conrad Estate, Doubleday & Co., Inc., New York, and J. M. Dent and Sons, Ltd., London.

It lies on me to confess at last, and this is as good a place for it as another, that I have been all my life—all my two lives—the spoiled adopted child of Great Britain and even of the Empire; for it was Australia that gave me my first command. I break out into this declaration not because of a lurking tendency to megalomania, but, on the contrary, as a man who has no very notable illusions about himself. I follow the instincts of vain-glory and humility natural to all mankind. For it can hardly be denied that it is not their own deserts that men are most proud of, but rather of their prodigious luck, of their marvellous fortune: of that in their lives for which thanks and sacrifices must be offered on the altars of the inscrutable gods.

Heart of Darkness also received a certain amount of notice from the first; and of its origins this much may be said: it is well known that curious men go prying into all sorts of places (where they have no business) and come out from them with all kinds of spoil. This story, and one other, not in this volume, are all the spoil I brought out from the centre of Africa, where, really, I had no sort of business. More ambitious in its scope and longer in the telling, *Heart of Darkness* is quite as authentic in fundamentals as *Youth*. It is, obviously, written in another mood. I won't characterise the mood precisely, but anybody can see that it is anything but the mood of wistful regret, of reminiscent tenderness.

One more remark may be added. *Youth* is a feat of memory. It is a record of experience; but that experience, in its facts, in its inwardness and in its outward colouring, begins and ends in myself. *Heart of Darkness* is experience too; but it is experience pushed a little (and only very little) beyond the actual facts of the case for the perfectly legitimate, I believe, purpose of bringing it home to the minds and bosoms of the readers. There it was no longer a matter of sincere colouring. It was like another art altogether. That sombre theme had to be given a sinister resonance, a tonality of its own, a continued vibration that, I hoped, would hang in the air and dwell on the ear after the last note had been struck.

After saying so much there remains the last tale of the book, still untouched. *The End of the Tether* is a story of sea-life in a rather special way; and the most intimate thing I can say of it is this: that having lived that life fully, amongst its men, its thoughts and sensations, I have found it possible, without the slightest misgiving, in all sincerity of heart and peace of conscience, to conceive the existence of Captain Whalley's personality and to relate the manner of his end. This statement acquires some force from the circumstance that the pages of that story—a fair half of the book—are also the product of experience. That experience belongs (like *Youth's*) to the time before I ever thought of putting pen to paper. As to its "reality," that is for the readers to determine. One had to pick up one's facts here and there. More skill would have made them more real and the whole composition more interesting. But here we are approaching the veiled region of artistic values which it would be improper and indeed dangerous for me to enter. I have looked over the proofs, have corrected a misprint or two, have changed a word or two—and that's all. It is not very likely that I shall ever read *The End of the Tether* again. No more need be said. It accords best with my feelings to part from Captain Whalley in affectionate silence.

J. C.

1917.

HEART OF DARKNESS*

Joseph Conrad

I

The *Nellie,* a cruising yawl, swung to her anchor without a flutter of the sails, and was at rest. The flood had made, the wind was nearly calm, and being bound down the river, the only thing for it was to come to and wait for the turn of the tide.

The sea-reach of the Thames stretched before us like the beginning of an interminable waterway. In the offing the sea and the sky were welded together without a joint, and in the luminous space the tanned sails of the barges drifting up with the tide seemed to stand still in red clusters of canvas sharply peaked, with gleams of varnished sprits. A haze rested on the low shores that ran out to sea in vanishing flatness. The air was dark above Gravesend, and farther back still seemed condensed into a mournful gloom, brooding motionless over the biggest, and the greatest, town on earth.

The Director of Companies was our captain and our host. We four affectionately watched his back as he stood in the bows looking to seaward. On the whole river there was nothing that looked half so nautical. He resembled a pilot, which to a seaman is trustworthiness personified. It was difficult to realise his work was not out there in the luminous estuary, but behind him, within the brooding gloom.

Between us there was, as I have already said somewhere, the bond of the sea. Besides holding our hearts together through long periods of separation, it had the effect of making us tolerant of each other's yarns—and even convictions. The Lawyer—the best of old fellows—had, because of his many years and many virtues, the only cushion on deck, and was lying on the only rug. The Accountant had brought out already a box of dominoes, and was toying architecturally with the bones. Marlow sat cross-legged right aft, leaning against the mizzen-mast. He had sunken cheeks, a yellow complexion, a straight back, an ascetic aspect, and, with his arms dropped, the palms of hands outwards, resembled an idol. The Director, satisfied the anchor had good hold, made his way aft and sat down amongst us. We exchanged a few words lazily. Afterwards there was silence on board the yacht. For some reason or other we did not begin that game of dominoes. We felt

---

* Reprinted from *Youth, A Narrative and Two Other Stories* with permission of the Trustees of the Joseph Conrad Estate, Doubleday & Co., Inc., New York, and J. M. Dent and Sons, Ltd., London.

meditative, and fit for nothing but placid staring. The day was ending in a serenity of still and exquisite brilliance. The water shone pacifically; the sky, without a speck, was a benign immensity of unstained light; the very mist on the Essex marshes was like a gauzy and radiant fabric, hung from the wooded rises inland, and draping the low shores in diaphanous folds. Only the gloom to the west, brooding over the upper reaches, became more sombre every minute, as if angered by the approach of the sun.

And at last, in its curved and imperceptible fall, the sun sank low, and from glowing white changed to a dull red without rays and without heat, as if about to go out suddenly, stricken to death by the touch of that gloom brooding over a crowd of men.

Forthwith a change came over the waters, and the serenity became less brilliant but more profound. The old river in its broad reach rested unruffled at the decline of day, after ages of good service done to the race that peopled its banks, spread out in the tranquil dignity of a waterway leading to the uttermost ends of the earth. We looked at the venerable stream not in the vivid flush of a short day that comes and departs for ever, but in the august light of abiding memories. And indeed nothing is easier for a man who has, as the phrase goes, "followed the sea" with reverence and affection, than to evoke the great spirit of the past upon the lower reaches of the Thames. The tidal current runs to and fro in its unceasing service, crowded with memories of men and ships it has borne to the rest of home or to the battles of the sea. It had known and served all the men of whom the nation is proud, from Sir Francis Drake to Sir John Franklin, knights all, titled and untitled—the great knights-errant of the sea. It had borne all the ships whose names are like jewels flashing in the night of time, from the *Golden Hind* returning with her round flanks full of treasure, to be visited by the Queen's Highness and thus pass out of the gigantic tale, to the *Erebus* and *Terror,* bound on other conquests—and that never returned. It had known the ships and the men. They had sailed from Deptford, from Greenwich, from Erith—the adventurers and the settlers; kings' ships and the ships of men on 'Change; captains, admirals, the dark "interlopers" of the Eastern trade, and the commissioned "generals" of East India fleets. Hunters for gold or pursuers of fame, they all had gone out on that stream, bearing the sword, and often the torch, messengers of the might within the land, bearers of a spark from the sacred fire. What greatness had not floated on the ebb of that river into the mystery of an unknown earth! . . . The dreams of men, the seed of commonwealths, the germs of empires.

The sun set; the dusk fell on the stream, and lights began to appear along the shore. The Chapman lighthouse, a three-legged thing erect on a mud-flat, shone strongly. Lights of ships moved in the fairway—a great stir of lights going up and going down. And farther west on the upper reaches the place of the monstrous town was still marked ominously on the sky, a brooding gloom in sunshine, a lurid glare under the stars.

"And this also," said Marlow suddenly, "has been one of the dark places of the earth."

He was the only man of us who still "followed the sea." The worst that could be said of him was that he did not represent his class. He was a seaman, but he was a wanderer too, while most seamen lead, if one may so express it, a sedentary life. Their minds are of the stay-at-home order, and their home is always with them—the ship; and so is their country—the sea. One ship is very much like another, and the sea is always the same. In the immutability of their surroundings the foreign shores, the foreign faces, the changing immensity of life, glide past, veiled not by a sense of mystery but by a slightly disdainful ignorance; for there is nothing mysterious to a seaman unless it be the sea itself, which is the mistress of his existence and as inscrutable as Destiny. For the rest, after his hours of work, a casual stroll or a casual spree on shore suffices to unfold for him the secret of a whole continent, and generally he finds the secret not worth knowing. The yarns of seamen have a direct simplicity, the whole meaning of which lies within the shell of a cracked nut. But Marlow was not typical (if his propensity to spin yarns be excepted), and to him the meaning of an episode was not inside like a kernel but outside, enveloping the tale which brought it out only as a glow brings out a haze, in the likeness of one of these misty halos that sometimes are made visible by the spectral illumination of moonshine.

His remark did not seem at all surprising. It was just like Marlow. It was accepted in silence. No one took the trouble to grunt even; and presently he said, very slow:

"I was thinking of very old times, when the Romans first came here, nineteen hundred years ago—the other day. . . . Light came out of this river since—you say Knights? Yes; but it is like a running blaze on a plain, like a flash of lightning in the clouds. We live in the flicker—may it last as long as the old earth keeps rolling! But darkness was here yesterday. Imagine the feelings of a commander of a fine—what d'ye call 'em?—trireme in the Mediterranean, ordered suddenly to the north; run overland across the Gauls in a hurry; put in charge of one of these craft the legionaries—a wonderful lot of handy men they must have been too—used to build, apparently by the hundred, in a month or two, if we may believe what we read. Imagine him here—the very end of the world, a sea the colour of lead, a sky the colour of smoke, a kind of ship about as rigid as a concertina—and going up this river with stores, or orders, or what you like. Sandbanks, marshes, forests, savages—precious little to eat fit for a civilised man, nothing but Thames water to drink. No Falernian wine here, no going ashore. Here and there a military camp lost in a wilderness, like a needle in a bundle of hay—cold, fog, tempests, disease, exile, and death—death skulking in the air, in the water, in the bush. They must have been dying like flies here. Oh yes—he did it. Did it very well, too, no doubt, and without thinking much about it either, except afterwards to brag of what he had gone through in his time, perhaps. They were men enough to face the darkness. And perhaps he was cheered by keeping his eye on a chance of promotion to the fleet at Ravenna by and by, if he had good friends in Rome and survived the awful climate. Or think of a decent young citizen in a toga—perhaps too much dice, you know—coming out here in the train of some prefect, or tax-gatherer, or trader, even, to mend his fortunes. Land in a swamp, march through the woods, and in some inland post feel the savagery, the utter savagery, had closed round him—all that mysterious life of the wilderness that stirs in the forest, in the jungles, in the hearts of wild men. There's no initiation either into such mysteries. He has to live in the midst of the incomprehensible, which is also detestable. And it has a fascination, too, that goes to work upon him. The fascination of the abomination—you know. Imagine the growing regrets, the longing to escape, the powerless disgust, the surrender, the hate."

He paused.

"Mind," he began again, lifting one arm from the elbow, the palm of the hand outwards, so that, with his legs folded before him, he had the pose of a Buddha preaching in European clothes and without a lotus-flower—"Mind, none of us would feel exactly like this. What saves us is efficiency—the devotion to efficiency. But these chaps were not much account, really. They were no colonists; their administration was merely a squeeze, and nothing more, I suspect. They were conquerors, and for that you want only brute force—nothing to boast of, when you have it, since your strength is just an accident arising from the weakness of others. They grabbed what they could get for the sake of what was to be got. It was just robbery with violence, aggravated murder on a great scale, and men going at it blind—as is very proper for those who tackle a darkness. The conquest of the earth, which mostly means the taking it away from those who have a different complexion or slightly flatter noses than ourselves, is not a pretty thing when you look into it too much. What redeems it is the idea only. An idea at the back of it; not a sentimental pretence but an idea; and an unselfish belief in the idea—something you can set up, and bow down before, and offer a sacrifice to. . . ."

He broke off. Flames glided in the river, small green flames, red flames, white flames, pursuing, overtaking, joining, crossing each other—then separating slowly or hastily. The traffic of the great city went on in the deepening night upon the sleepless river. We looked on, waiting patiently—there was nothing else to do till the end of the flood; but it was only after a long silence, when he said, in a hesitating voice, "I suppose you fellows remember I did once turn fresh-water sailor for a bit," that we knew we were fated, before the ebb began to run, to hear about one of Marlow's inconclusive experiences.

"I don't want to bother you much with what happened to me personally," he began, showing in this remark the weakness of many tellers of tales who seem so often unaware of what their audience would best like to hear; "yet to understand the effect of it on me you ought to know how I got out there, what I saw, how I went up that river to the place where I first met the poor chap. It was the farthest point of navigation and the culminating point of my experience. It seemed somehow to throw a kind of light on everything about me—and into my thoughts. It was sombre enough too—and pitiful—not extraordinary in any way—not very clear either. No, not very clear. And yet it seemed to throw a kind of light.

"I had then, as you remember, just returned to London after a lot of Indian Ocean, Pacific, China Seas—a regular dose of the East—six years or so, and I was loafing about, hindering you fellows in your work and invading your homes, just as though I had got a heavenly mission to civilise you. It was very fine for a time, but after a bit I did get tired of resting. Then I began to look for a ship—I should think the hardest work on earth. But the ships wouldn't even look at me. And I got tired of that game too.

"Now when I was a little chap I had a passion for maps. I would look for hours at South America, or Africa, or Australia, and lose myself in all the glories of exploration. At that time there were many blank spaces on the earth, and when I saw one that looked particularly inviting on a map (but they all look that) I would put my finger on it and say, When I grow up I will go there. The North Pole was one of these places, I remember. Well, I haven't been there yet, and shall not try now. The glamour's off. Other places were scattered about the Equator, and in every sort of latitude all over the two hemispheres. I have been in some of them, and . . . well, we won't talk about that. But there was one yet—the biggest, the most blank, so to speak—that I had a hankering after.

"True, by this time it was not a blank space any more. It had got filled since my boyhood with rivers and lakes and names. It had ceased to be a blank space of delightful mystery—a white patch for a boy to dream gloriously over. It had become a place of darkness. But there was in it one river especially, a mighty big river, that you could see on the map, resembling an immense snake uncoiled, with its head in the sea, its body at rest curving afar over a vast country, and its tail lost in the depths of the land. And as I looked at the map of it in a shop-window, it fascinated me as a snake would a bird—a silly little bird. Then I remembered there was a big concern, a Company for trade on that river. Dash it all! I thought to myself, they can't trade without using some kind of craft on that lot of fresh water—steamboats! Why shouldn't I try to get charge of one? I went on along Fleet Street, but could not shake off the idea. The snake had charmed me.

"You understand it was a Continental concern, that Trading

Society; but I have a lot of relations living on the Continent, because it's cheap and not so nasty as it looks, they say.

"I am sorry to own I began to worry them. This was already a fresh departure for me. I was not used to get things that way, you know. I always went my own road and on my own legs where I had a mind to go. I wouldn't have believed it of myself; but, then—you see—I felt somehow I must get there by hook or by crook. So I worried them. The men said, 'My dear fellow,' and did nothing. Then—would you believe it?—I tried the women. I, Charlie Marlow, set the women to work—to get a job. Heavens! Well, you see, the notion drove me. I had an aunt, a dear enthusiastic soul. She wrote: 'It will be delightful. I am ready to do anything, anything for you. It is a glorious idea. I know the wife of a very high personage in the Administration, and also a man who has lots of influence with,' etc. etc. She was determined to make no end of fuss to get me appointed skipper of a river steamboat, if such was my fancy.

"I got my appointment—of course; and I got it very quick. It appears the Company had received news that one of their captains had been killed in a scuffle with the natives. This was my chance, and it made me the more anxious to go. It was only months and months afterwards, when I made the attempt to recover what was left of the body, that I heard the original quarrel arose from a misunderstanding about some hens. Yes, two black hens. Fresleven—that was the fellow's name, a Dane—thought himself wronged somehow in the bargain, so he went ashore and started to hammer the chief of the village with a stick. Oh, it didn't surprise me in the least to hear this, and at the same time to be told that Fresleven was the gentlest, quietest creature that ever walked on two legs. No doubt he was; but he had been a couple of years already out there engaged in the noble cause, you know, and he probably felt the need at last of asserting his self-respect in some way. Therefore he whacked the old nigger mercilessly, while a big crowd of his people watched him, thunderstruck, till some man—I was told the chief's son—in desperation at hearing the old chap yell, made a tentative jab with a spear at the white man—and of course it went quite easy between the shoulder-blades. Then the whole population cleared into the forest, expecting all kinds of calamities to happen, while, on the other hand, the steamer Fresleven commanded left also in a bad panic, in charge of the engineer, I believe. Afterwards nobody seemed to trouble much about Fresleven's remains, till I got out and stepped into his shoes. I couldn't let it rest, though; but when an opportunity offered at last to meet my predecessor, the grass growing through his ribs was tall enough to hide his bones. They were all there. The supernatural being had not been touched after he fell. And the village was deserted, the huts gaped black, rotting, all askew within the fallen enclosures. A calamity had come to it, sure enough. The people had vanished. Mad terror had scattered them, men, women, and children, through the bush, and they had never returned. What became of the hens I don't know either. I should think the cause of progress got them, anyhow. However, through this glorious affair I got my appointment, before I had fairly begun to hope for it.

"I flew around like mad to get ready, and before forty-eight hours I was crossing the Channel to show myself to my employers, and sign the contract. In a very few hours I arrived in a city that always makes me think of a whited sepulchre. Prejudice no doubt. I had no difficulty in finding the Company's offices. It was the biggest thing in the town, and everybody I met was full of it. They were going to run an over-sea empire, and make no end of coin by trade.

"A narrow and deserted street in deep shadow, high houses, innumerable windows with venetian blinds, a dead silence, grass sprouting between the stones, imposing carriage archways right and left, immense double doors standing ponderously ajar. I slipped through one of these cracks, went up a swept and ungarnished staircase, as arid as a desert, and opened the first door I came to. Two women, one fat and the other slim, sat on straw-bottomed chairs, knitting black wool. The slim one got up and walked straight at me—still knitting with down-cast eyes—and only just as I began to think of getting out of her way, as you would for a somnambulist, stood still, and looked up. Her dress was as plain as an umbrella-cover, and she turned round without a word and preceded me into a waiting-room. I gave my name, and looked about. Deal table in the middle, plain chairs all round the walls, on one end a large shining map, marked with all the colours of a rainbow. There was a vast amount of red—good to see at any time, because one knows that some real work is done in there, a deuce of a lot of blue, a little green, smears of orange, and, on the East Coast, a purple patch, to show where the jolly pioneers of progress drink the jolly lager-beer. However, I wasn't going into any of these. I was going into the yellow. Dead in the centre. And the river was there—fascinating—deadly—like a snake. Ough! A door opened, a white-haired secretarial head, but wearing a compassionate expression, appeared, and a skinny forefinger beckoned me into the sanctuary. Its light was dim, and a heavy writing-desk squatted in the middle. From behind that structure came out an impression of pale plumpness in a frock-coat. The great man himself. He was five feet six, I should judge, and had his grip on the handle-end of ever so many millions. He shook hands, I fancy, murmured vaguely, was satisfied with my French. *Bon voyage.*

"In about forty-five seconds I found myself again in the waiting-room with the compassionate secretary, who, full of desolation and sympathy, made me sign some document. I believe I undertook amongst other things not to disclose any trade secrets. Well, I am not going to.

"I began to feel slightly uneasy. You know I am not used to such ceremonies, and there was something ominous in the atmosphere. It was just as though I had been let into some conspiracy—I don't know—something not quite right; and I was glad to get out. In the outer room the two women knitted black wool feverishly. People were arriving, and the younger one was walking back and forth introducing them. The old one sat on her chair. Her flat cloth slippers were propped up on a foot-warmer, and a cat reposed on her lap. She wore a starched white affair on her head, had a wart on one cheek, and silver-rimmed spectacles hung on the tip of her nose. She glanced at me above the glasses. The swift and indifferent placidity of that look troubled me. Two youths with foolish and cheery countenances were being piloted over, and she threw at them the same quick glance of unconcerned wisdom. She seemed to know all about them and about me too. An eerie feeling came over me. She seemed uncanny and fateful. Often far away there I thought of these two, guarding the door of Darkness, knitting black wool as for a warm pall, one introducing, introducing continuously to the unknown, the other scrutinising the cheery and foolish faces with unconcerned old eyes. *Ave!* Old knitter of black wool. *Morituri te salutant.* Not many of those she looked at ever saw her again—not half, by a long way.

"There was yet a visit to the doctor. 'A simple formality,' assured me the secretary, with an air of taking an immense part in all my sorrows. Accordingly a young chap wearing his hat over the left eyebrow, some clerk I suppose—there must have been clerks in the business, though the house was as still as a house in a city of the dead—came from somewhere upstairs, and led me forth. He was shabby and careless, with ink-stains on the sleeves of his jacket, and his cravat was large and billowy, under a chin shaped like the toe of an old boot. It was a little too early for the doctor, so I proposed a drink, and thereupon he developed a vein of joviality. As we sat over our vermuths he glorified the Company's business, and by and by I expressed casually my surprise at him not going out there. He became very cool and collected all at once. 'I am not such a fool as I look, quoth Plato to his disciples,' he said sententiously, emptied his glass with great resolution, and we rose.

"The old doctor felt my pulse, evidently thinking of something else the while. 'Good, good for there,' he mumbled, and then with a certain eagerness asked me whether I would let him measure my head. Rather surprised, I said Yes, when he produced a thing like callipers and got the dimensions back and front and every way, taking notes carefully. He was an unshaven little man in a threadbare coat like a gaberdine, with his feet in slippers, and I thought him a harmless fool. 'I always ask leave, in the interests of science, to measure the crania of those going out there,' he said. 'And when they come back too?' I asked. 'Oh, I never see them,' he remarked; 'and, moreover, the changes take place inside, you know.' He smiled, as if at some quiet joke. 'So you are going out there. Famous. Interesting too.' He gave me a searching glance, and made another note. 'Ever any madness in your family?' he asked, in a matter-of-fact tone. I felt very annoyed. 'Is that question in the interests of science too?' 'It would be,' he said, without taking notice of my irritation, 'interesting for science to watch the mental changes of individuals, on the spot, but . . .' 'Are you an alienist?' I interrupted. 'Every doctor should be—a little,' answered that original imperturbably. 'I have a little theory which you Messieurs who go out there must help me to prove. This is my share in the advantages my country shall reap from the possession of such a magnificent dependency. The mere wealth I leave to others. Pardon my questions, but you are the first Englishman coming under my observation . . .' I hastened to assure him I was not in the least typical. 'If I were,' said I, 'I wouldn't be talking like this with you.' 'What you say is rather profound, and probably erroneous,' he said, with a laugh. 'Avoid irritation more than exposure to the sun. Adieu. How do you English say, eh? Good-bye. Ah! Good-bye. Adieu. In the tropics one must before everything keep calm.' . . . He lifted a warning forefinger. . . . '*Du calme, du calme. Adieu.*'

"One thing more remained to do—say good-bye to my excellent aunt. I found her triumphant. I had a cup of tea—the last decent cup of tea for many days—and in a room that most soothingly looked just as you would expect a lady's drawing-room to look, we had a long quiet chat by the fireside. In the course of these confidences it became quite plain to me I had been represented to the wife of the high dignitary, and goodness knows to how many more people besides, as an exceptional and gifted creature—a piece of good fortune for the Company—a man you don't get hold of every day. Good heavens! and I was going to take charge of a two-penny-halfpenny river-steamboat with a penny whistle attached! It appeared, however, I was also one of the Workers, with a capital—you know. Something like an emissary of light, something like a lower sort of apostle. There had been a lot of such rot let loose in print and talk just about that time, and the excellent woman, living right in the rush of all that humbug, got carried off her feet. She talked about 'weaning those ignorant millions from their horrid ways,' till, upon my word, she made me quite uncomfortable. I ventured to hint that the Company was run for profit.

" 'You forget, dear Charlie, that the labourer is worthy of his hire,' she said brightly. It's queer how out of touch with truth women are. They live in a world of their own, and there had never been anything like it, and never can be. It is too beautiful altogether, and if they were to set it up it would go to pieces before the first sunset. Some confounded fact we men have been living contentedly with ever since the day of creation would start up and knock the whole thing over.

"After this I got embraced, told to wear flannel, be sure to write often, and so on—and I left. In the street—I don't know why—a queer feeling came to me that I was an impostor. Odd thing that I, who used to clear out for any part of the world at twenty-four hours' notice, with less thought than most men give to the crossing of a street, had a moment—I won't say of hesitation, but of startled pause, before this commonplace affair. The best way I can explain it to you is by saying that, for a second or two, I felt as though, instead of going to the centre of a continent, I were about to set off for the centre of the earth.

"I left in a French steamer, and she called in every blamed port they have out there, for, as far as I could see, the sole purpose of landing soldiers and custom-house officers. I watched the coast. Watching a coast as it slips by the ship is like thinking about an enigma. There it is before you—smiling, frowning, inviting, grand, mean, insipid, or savage, and always mute with an air of whispering, Come and find out. This one was almost featureless, as if still in the making, with an aspect of monotonous grimness. The edge of a colossal jungle, so dark green as to be almost black, fringed with white surf, ran straight, like a ruled line, far, far away along a blue sea whose glitter was blurred by a creeping mist. The sun was fierce, the land seemed to glisten and drip with steam. Here and there greyish-whitish specks showed up clustered inside the white surf, with a flag flying above them perhaps—settlements some centuries old, and still no bigger than pin-heads on the untouched expanse of their background. We pounded along, stopped, landed soldiers; went on, landed custom-house clerks to levy toll in what looked like a God-forsaken wilderness, with a tin shed and a flag-pole lost in it; landed more soldiers—to take care of the custom-house clerks presumably. Some, I heard, got drowned in the surf; but whether they did or not, nobody seemed particularly to care. They were just flung out there, and on we went. Every day the coast looked the same, as though we had not moved; but we passed various places—trading places—with names like Gran' Bassam, Little Popo; names that seemed to belong to some sordid farce acted in front of a sinister back-cloth. The idleness of a passenger, my isolation amongst all these men with whom I had no point of contact, the oily and languid sea, the uniform sombreness of the coast, seemed to keep me away from the truth of things, within the toil of a mournful and senseless delusion. The voice of the surf heard now and then was a positive pleasure, like the speech of a brother. It was something natural, that had its reason, that had a meaning. Now and then a boat from the shore gave one a momentary contact with reality. It was paddled by black fellows. You could see from afar the white of their eyeballs glistening. They shouted, sang; their bodies streamed with perspiration; they had faces like grotesque masks—these chaps; but they had bone, muscle, a wild vitality, an intense energy of movement, that was as natural and true as the surf along their coast. They wanted no excuse for being there. They were a great comfort to look at. For a time I would feel I belonged still to a world of straightforward facts; but the feeling would not last long. Something would turn up to scare it away. Once, I remember, we came upon a man-of-war anchored off the coast. There wasn't even a shed there, and she was shelling the bush. It appears the French had one of their wars going on thereabouts. Her ensign dropped limp like a rag; the muzzles of the long six-inch guns stuck out all over the low hull; the greasy, slimy swell swung her up lazily and let her down, swaying her thin masts. In the empty immensity of earth, sky, and water, there she was, incomprehensible, firing into a continent. Pop, would go one of the six-inch guns; a small flame would dart and vanish, a little white smoke would disappear, a tiny projectile would give a feeble screech—and nothing happened. Nothing could happen. There was a touch of insanity in the proceeding, a sense of lugubrious drollery in the sight; and it was not dissipated by somebody on board assuring me earnestly there was a camp of natives—he called them enemies!—hidden out of sight somewhere.

"We gave her her letters (I heard the men in that lonely ship were dying of fever at the rate of three a day) and went on. We called at some more places with farcical names, where the merry dance of death and trade goes on in a still and earthy atmosphere as of an overheated catacomb; all along the formless coast bordered by dangerous surf, as if Nature herself had tried to ward off intruders; in and out of rivers, streams of death in life, whose banks were rotting into mud, whose waters, thickened into slime, invaded the contorted mangroves, that seemed to writhe at us in the extremity of an impotent despair. Nowhere did we stop long enough to get a particularised impression, but the general sense of vague and oppressive wonder grew upon me. It was like a weary pilgrimage amongst hints for nightmares.

"It was upward of thirty days before I saw the mouth of the big river. We anchored off the seat of the government. But my work would not begin till some two hundred miles farther on. So as soon as I could I made a start for a place thirty miles higher up.

"I had my passage on a little sea-going steamer. Her captain was a Swede, and knowing me for a seaman, invited me on the bridge. He was a young man, lean, fair, and morose, with lanky hair and a shuffling gait. As we left the miserable little wharf, he tossed his head contemptuously at the shore. 'Been living there?' he asked. I said, 'Yes.' 'Fine lot these government chaps—are they not?' he went on, speaking English with great precision and considerable bitterness. 'It is funny what some people will do for a few francs a month. I wonder what becomes of that kind when it goes up country?' I said to him I expected to see that soon. 'So-o-o!' he exclaimed. He shuffled athwart, keeping one eye ahead vigilantly. 'Don't be too sure,' he continued. 'The other day I took up a man who hanged himself on the road. He was a Swede, too.' 'Hanged himself! Why, in God's name?' I cried. He

kept on looking out watchfully. 'Who knows? The sun too much for him, or the country perhaps.'

"At last we opened a reach. A rocky cliff appeared, mounds of turned-up earth by the shore, houses on a hill, others with iron roofs, amongst a waste of excavations, or hanging to the declivity. A continuous noise of the rapids above hovered over this scene of inhabited devastation. A lot of people, mostly black and naked, moved about like ants. A jetty projected into the river. A blinding sunlight drowned all this at times in a sudden recrudescence of glare. 'There's your Company's station,' said the Swede, pointing to three wooden barrack-like structures on the rocky slope. 'I will send your things up. Four boxes did you say? So. Farewell.'

"I came upon a boiler wallowing in the grass, then found a path leading up the hill. It turned aside for the boulders, and also for an undersized railway truck lying there on its back with its wheels in the air. One was off. The thing looked as dead as the carcass of some animal. I came upon more pieces of decaying machinery, a stack of rusty nails. To the left a clump of trees made a shady spot, where dark things seemed to stir feebly. I blinked, the path was steep. A horn tooted to the right, and I saw the black people run. A heavy and dull detonation shook the ground, a puff of smoke came out of the cliff, and that was all. No change appeared on the face of the rock. They were building a railway. The cliff was not in the way or anything; but this objectless blasting was all the work going on.

"A slight clinking behind me made me turn my head. Six black men advanced in a file, toiling up the path. They walked erect and slow, balancing small baskets full of earth on their heads, and the clink kept time with their footsteps. Black rags were wound round their loins, and the short ends behind waggled to and fro like tails. I could see every rib, the joints of their limbs were like knots in a rope; each had an iron collar on his neck, and all were connected together with a chain whose bights swung between them, rhythmically clinking. Another report from the cliff made me think suddenly of that ship of war I had seen firing into a continent. It was the same kind of ominous voice; but these men could by no stretch of imagination be called enemies. They were called criminals, and the outraged law, like the bursting shells, had come to them, an insoluble mystery from the sea. All their meagre breasts panted together, the violently dilated nostrils quivered, the eyes stared stonily uphill. They passed me within six inches, without a glance, with that complete, deathlike indifference of unhappy savages. Behind this raw matter one of the reclaimed, the product of the new forces at work, strolled despondently, carrying a rifle by its middle. He had a uniform jacket with one button off, and seeing a white man on the path, hoisted his weapon to his shoulder with alacrity. This was simple prudence, white men being so much alike at a distance that he could not tell who I might be. He was speedily reassured, and with a large, white, rascally grin, and a glance at his charge, seemed to take me into partnership in his exalted trust. After all, I also was a part of the great cause of these high and just proceedings.

"Instead of going up, I turned and descended to the left. My idea was to let that chain-gang get out of sight before I climbed the hill. You know I am not particularly tender; I've had to strike and to fend off. I've had to resist and to attack sometimes—that's only one way of resisting—without counting the exact cost, according to the demands of such sort of life as I had blundered into. I've seen the devil of violence, and the devil of greed, and the devil of hot desire; but, by all the stars! these were strong, lusty, red-eyed devils, that swayed and drove men—men, I tell you. But as I stood on this hillside, I foresaw that in the blinding sunshine of that land I would become acquainted with a flabby, pretending, weak-eyed devil of a rapacious and pitiless folly. How insidious he could be, too, I was only to find out several months later and a thousand miles farther. For a moment I stood appalled, as though by a warning. Finally I descended the hill, obliquely, towards the trees I had seen.

"I avoided a vast artificial hole somebody had been digging on the slope, the purpose of which I found it impossible to divine. It wasn't a quarry or a sandpit, anyhow. It was just a hole. It might have been connected with the philanthropic desire of giving the criminals something to do. I don't know. Then I nearly fell into a very narrow ravine, almost no more than a scar in the hillside. I discovered that a lot of imported drainage-pipes for the settlement had been tumbled in there. There wasn't one that was not broken. It was a wanton smash-up. At last I got under the trees. My purpose was to stroll into the shade for a moment; but no sooner within than it seemed to me I had stepped into the gloomy circle of some Inferno. The rapids were near, and an uninterrupted, uniform, headlong, rushing noise filled the mournful stillness of the grove, where not a breath stirred, not a leaf moved, with a mysterious sound—as though the tearing pace of the launched earth had suddenly become audible.

"Black shapes crouched, lay, sat between the trees, leaning against the trunks, clinging to the earth, half coming out, half effaced within the dim light, in all the attitudes of pain, abandonment, and despair. Another mine on the cliff went off, followed by a slight shudder of the soil under my feet. The work was going on. The work! And this was the place where some of the helpers had withdrawn to die.

"They were dying slowly—it was very clear. They were not enemies, they were not criminals, they were nothing earthly now—nothing but black shadows of disease and starvation, lying confusedly in the greenish gloom. Brought from all the recesses of the coast in all the legality of time contracts, lost in uncongenial surroundings, fed on unfamiliar food, they sickened, became inefficient, and were then allowed to crawl away and rest. These moribund shapes were free as air—and nearly as thin. I began to distinguish the gleam of eyes under the trees. Then, glancing down, I saw a face near my hand. The black bones reclined at full length with one shoulder against the tree, and slowly the eyelids rose and the sunken eyes looked up at me, enormous and vacant, a kind of blind, white flicker in the depths of the orbs, which died out slowly. The man seemed young—almost a boy—but you know with them it's hard to tell. I found nothing else to do but to offer him one of my good Swede's ship's biscuits I had in my pocket. The fingers closed slowly on it and held—there was no other movement and no other glance. He had tied a bit of white worsted round his neck—Why? Where did he get it? Was it a badge—an ornament—a charm—a propitiatory act? Was there any idea at all connected with it? It looked startling round his black neck, this bit of white thread from beyond the seas.

"Near the same tree two more bundles of acute angles sat with their legs drawn up. One, with his chin propped on his knees, stared at nothing, in an intolerable and appalling manner: his brother phantom rested its forehead, as if overcome with a great weariness; and all about others were scattered in every pose of contorted collapse, as in some picture of a massacre or a pestilence. While I stood horror-struck, one of these creatures rose to his hands and knees, and went off on all-fours towards the river to drink. He lapped out of his hand, then sat up in the sunlight, crossing his shins in front of him, and after a time let his woolly head fall on his breastbone.

"I didn't want any more loitering in the shade, and I made haste towards the station. When near the buildings I met a white man, in such an unexpected elegance of get-up that in the first moment I took him for a sort of vision. I saw a high starched collar, white cuffs, a light alpaca jacket, snowy trousers, a clear necktie, and varnished boots. No hat. Hair parted, brushed, oiled, under a green-lined parasol held in a big white hand. He was amazing, and had a penholder behind his ear.

"I shook hands with this miracle, and I learned he was the Company's chief accountant, and that all the book-keeping was done at this station. He had come out for a moment, he said, 'to get a breath of fresh air.' The expression sounded wonderfully odd, with its suggestion of sedentary desk-life. I wouldn't have mentioned the fellow to you at all, only it was from his lips that I first heard the name of the man who is so indissolubly connected with the memories of that time. Moreover, I respected the fellow. Yes; I respected his collars, his vast cuffs, his brushed hair. His appearance was certainly that of a hairdresser's dummy; but in the great demoralisation of the land he kept up his appearance. That's backbone. His starched collars and got-up shirt-fronts were achievements of character. He had been out nearly three years; and, later, I could not help asking him how he managed to sport such linen. He had just the faintest blush, and said modestly, 'I've been teaching one of the native women about the station. It was difficult. She had a distaste for the work.' Thus this man had verily accomplished something. And he was devoted to his books, which were in apple-pie order.

"Everything else in the station was in a muddle,—heads, things, buildings. Strings of dusty niggers with splay feet arrived and departed; a stream of manufactured goods, rubbishy cottons, beads, and brass-wire set into the depths of darkness, and in return came a precious trickle of ivory.

"I had to wait in the station for ten days—an eternity. I lived in a hut in the yard, but to be out of the chaos I would sometimes get into the accountant's office. It was built of horizontal planks, and so badly put together that, as he bent over his high desk, he was barred from neck to heels with narrow strips of sunlight. There was no need to open the big shutter to see. It was hot there too; big flies buzzed fiendishly, and did not sting, but stabbed. I sat generally on the floor, while, of faultless appearance (and even slightly scented), perching on a high stool, he wrote, he wrote. Sometimes he stood up for exercise. When a truckle-bed with a sick man (some invalided agent from up-country) was put in there, he exhibited a gentle annoyance. 'The groans of this sick person,' he said, 'distract my attention. And without that it is extremely difficult to guard against clerical errors in this climate.'

"One day he remarked, without lifting his head, 'In the interior you will no doubt meet Mr. Kurtz.' On my asking who Mr. Kurtz was, he said he was a first-class agent; and seeing my disappointment at this information, he added slowly, laying down his pen, 'He is a very remarkable person.' Further questions elicited from him that Mr. Kurtz was at present in charge of a trading-post, a very important one, in the true ivory-country, at 'the very bottom of there. Sends in as much ivory as all the others put together . . .' He began to write again. The sick man was too ill to groan. The flies buzzed in a great peace.

"Suddenly there was a growing murmur of voices and a great tramping of feet. A caravan had come in. A violent babble of uncouth sounds burst out on the other side of the planks. All the carriers were speaking together, and in the midst of the uproar the lamentable voice of the chief agent was heard 'giving it up' tearfully for the twentieth time that day. . . . He rose slowly. 'What a frightful row,' he said. He crossed the room gently to look at the sick man, and returning, said to me, 'He does not hear.' 'What! Dead?' I asked, startled. 'No, not yet,' he answered, with great composure. Then, alluding with a toss of the head to the tumult in the station-yard, 'When one has got to make correct entries, one comes to hate those savages—hate them to the death.' He remained thoughtful for a moment. 'When you see Mr. Kurtz,' he went on, 'tell him from me that everything here'—he glanced at the desk—'is very satisfactory. I don't like to write to him—with those messengers of ours you never know who may get hold of your letter—at that Central Station.' He stared at me for a moment with his mild, bulging eyes. 'Oh, he will go far, very far,' he began again. 'He will be a somebody in the Administration before long. They, above—the Council in Europe, you know—mean him to be.'

"He turned to his work. The noise outside had ceased, and presently in going out I stopped at the door. In the steady buzz of flies the homeward-bound agent was lying flushed and insensible; the other, bent over his books, was making correct entries of perfectly correct transactions; and fifty feet below the doorstep I could see the still tree-tops of the grove of death.

"Next day I left that station at last, with a caravan of sixty men, for a two-hundred-mile tramp.

"No use telling you much about that. Paths, paths, everywhere; a stamped-in network of paths spreading over the empty land, through long grass, through burnt grass, through thickets, down and up chilly ravines, up and down stony hills ablaze with heat; and a solitude, a solitude, nobody, not a hut. The population had cleared out a long time ago. Well, if a lot of mysterious niggers armed with all kinds of fearful weapons suddenly took to travelling on the road between Deal and Gravesend, catching the yokels right and left to carry heavy loads for them, I fancy every farm and cottage thereabouts would get empty very soon. Only here the dwellings were gone too. Still, I passed through several abandoned villages. There's something pathetically childish in the ruins of grass walls. Day after day, with the stamp and shuffle of sixty pair of bare feet behind me, each pair under a 60-lb. load. Camp, cook, sleep, strike camp, march. Now and then a carrier dead in harness, at rest in the long grass near the path, with an empty water-gourd and his long staff lying by his side. A great silence around and above. Perhaps on some quiet night the tremor of far-off drums, sinking, swelling, a tremor vast, faint; a sound weird, appealing, suggestive, and wild—and perhaps with as profound a meaning as the sound of bells in a Christian country. Once a white man in an unbuttoned uniform, camping on the path with an armed escort of lank Zanzibaris, very hospitable and festive—not to say drunk. Was looking after the upkeep of the road, he declared. Can't say I saw any road or any upkeep, unless the body of a middle-aged negro, with a bullet-hole in the forehead, upon which I absolutely stumbled three miles farther on, may be considered as a permanent improvement. I had a white companion too, not a bad chap, but rather too fleshy and with the exasperating habit of fainting on the hot hillsides, miles away from the least bit of shade and water. Annoying, you know, to hold your own coat like a parasol over a man's head while he is coming-to. I couldn't help asking him once what he meant by coming there at all. 'To make money, of course. What do you think?' he said scornfully.

Then he got fever, and had to be carried in a hammock slung under a pole. As he weighed sixteen stone I had no end of rows with the carriers. They jibbed, ran away, sneaked off with their loads in the night—quite a mutiny. So, one evening, I made a speech in English with gestures, not one of which was lost to the sixty pairs of eyes before me, and the next morning I started the hammock off in front all right. An hour afterwards I came upon the whole concern wrecked in a bush—man, hammock, groans, blankets, horrors. The heavy pole had skinned his poor nose. He was very anxious for me to kill somebody, but there wasn't the shadow of a carrier near. I remembered the old doctor—'It would be interesting for science to watch the mental changes of individuals, on the spot.' I felt I was becoming scientifically interesting. However, all that is to no purpose. On the fifteenth day I came in sight of the big river again, and hobbled into the Central Station. It was on a back water surrounded by scrub and forest, with a pretty border of smelly mud on one side, and on the three others enclosed by a crazy fence of rushes. A neglected gap was all the gate it had, and the first glance at the place was enough to let you see the flabby devil was running that show. White men with long staves in their hands appeared languidly from amongst the buildings, strolling up to take a look at me, and then retired out of sight somewhere. One of them, a stout, excitable chap with black moustaches, informed me with great volubility and many digressions, as soon as I told him who I was, that my steamer was at the bottom of the river. I was thunderstruck. What, how, why? Oh, it was 'all right.' The 'manager himself' was there. All quite correct. 'Everybody had behaved splendidly! splendidly!'—'You must,' he said in agitation, 'go and see the general manager at once. He is waiting!'

"I did not see the real significance of that wreck at once. I fancy I see it now, but I am not sure—not at all. Certainly the affair was too stupid—when I think of it—to be altogether natural. Still . . . But at the moment it presented itself simply as a confounded nuisance. The steamer was sunk. They had started two days before in a sudden hurry up the river with the manager on board, in charge of some volunteer skipper, and before they had been out three hours they tore the bottom out of her on stones, and she sank near the south bank. I asked myself what I was to do there, now my boat was lost. As a matter of fact, I had plenty to do in fishing my command out of the river. I had to set about it the very next day. That, and the repairs when I brought the pieces to the station, took some months.

"My first interview with the manager was curious. He did not ask me to sit down after my twenty-mile walk that morning. He was commonplace in complexion, in feature, in manners, and in voice. He was of middle size and of ordinary build. His eyes, of the usual blue, were perhaps remarkably cold, and he certainly could make his glance fall on one as trenchant and heavy as an axe. But even at these times the rest of his person seemed to disclaim the intention. Otherwise there was only an indefinable, faint expression of his lips, something stealthy—a smile—not a smile—I remember it, but I can't explain. It was unconscious, this smile was, though just after he had said something it got intensified for an instant. It came at the end of his speeches like a seal applied on the words to make the meaning of the commonest phrase appear absolutely inscrutable. He was a common trader, from his youth up employed in these parts—nothing more. He was obeyed, yet he inspired neither love nor fear, nor even respect. He inspired uneasiness. That was it! Uneasiness. Not a definite mistrust—just uneasiness—nothing more. You have no idea how effective such a . . . a . . . faculty can be. He had no genius for organising, for initiative, or for order even. That was evident in such things as the deplorable state of the station. He had no learning, and no intelligence. His position had come to him—why? Perhaps because he was never ill . . . He had served three terms of three years out there . . . Because triumphant health in the general rout of constitutions is a kind of power in itself. When he went home on leave he rioted on a large scale—pompously. Jack ashore—with a difference—in externals only. This one could gather from his casual talk. He originated nothing, he could keep the routine going—that's all. But he was great. He was great by this little thing that it was impossible to tell what could control such a man. He never gave that secret away. Perhaps there was nothing within him. Such a suspicion made one pause—for out there there were no external checks. Once when various tropical diseases had laid low almost every 'agent' in the station, he was heard to say, 'Men who come out here should have no entrails.' He sealed the utterance with that smile of his, as though it had been a door opening into a darkness he had in his keeping. You fancied you had seen things—but the seal was on. When annoyed at meal-times by the constant quarrels of the white men about precedence, he ordered an immense round table to be made, for which a special house had to be built. This was the station's mess-room. Where he sat was the first place—the rest were nowhere. One felt this to be his unalterable conviction. He was neither civil nor uncivil. He was quiet. He allowed his 'boy'—an overfed young negro from the coast—to treat the white men, under his very eyes, with provoking insolence.

"He began to speak as soon as he saw me. I had been very long on the road. He could not wait. Had to start without me. The up-river stations had to be relieved. There had been so many delays already that he did not know who was dead and who was alive, and how they got on—and so on, and so on. He paid no attention to my explanations, and, playing with a stick of sealing-wax, repeated several times that the situation was 'very grave, very grave.' There were rumours that a very important station was in jeopardy, and its chief, Mr. Kurtz, was ill. Hoped it was not true. Mr. Kurtz was . . . I felt weary and irritable. Hang Kurtz, I thought. I interrupted him by saying I had heard of Mr. Kurtz on the coast. 'Ah! So they talk of him down there,' he murmured to himself. Then he began again, assuring me Mr. Kurtz was the best agent he had, an exceptional man, of the greatest importance to the Company; therefore I could understand his anxiety. He was, he said, 'very, very uneasy.' Certainly he fidgeted on his chair a good deal, exclaimed, 'Ah, Mr. Kurtz!' broke the stick of sealing-wax and seemed dumbfounded by the accident. Next thing he wanted to know 'how long it would take to' . . . I interrupted him again. Being hungry, you know, and kept on my feet too, I was getting savage. 'How can I tell?' I said. 'I haven't even seen the wreck yet—some months, no doubt.' All this talk seemed to me so futile. 'Some months,' he said. 'Well, let us say three months before we can make a start. Yes. That ought to do the affair.' I flung out of his hut (he lived all alone in a clay hut with a sort of verandah) muttering to myself my opinion of him. He was a chattering idiot. Afterwards I took it back when it was borne in upon me startlingly with what extreme nicety he had estimated the time requisite for the 'affair.'

"I went to work the next day, turning, so to speak, my back on that station. In that way only it seemed to me I could keep my hold on the redeeming facts of life. Still, one must look about sometimes; and then I saw this station, these men strolling aimlessly about in the sunshine of the yard. I asked myself sometimes what it all meant. They wandered here and there with their absurd long staves in their hands, like a lot of faithless pilgrims bewitched inside a rotten fence. The word 'ivory' rang in the air, was whispered, was sighed. You would think they were praying to it. A taint of imbecile rapacity blew through it all, like a whiff from some corpse. By Jove! I've never seen anything so unreal in my life. And outside, the silent wilderness surrounding this cleared speck on the earth struck me as something great and invincible, like evil or truth, waiting patiently for the passing away of this fantastic invasion.

"Oh, these months! Well, never mind. Various things happened. One evening a grass shed full of calico, cotton prints, beads, and I don't know what else, burst into a blaze so suddenly that you would have thought the earth had opened to let an avenging fire consume all that trash. I was smoking my pipe quietly by my dismantled steamer, and saw them all cutting capers in the light, with their arms lifted high, when the stout man with moustaches came tearing down to the river, a tin pail in his hand, assured me that everybody was 'behaving splendidly, splendidly,' dipped about a quart of water and tore back again. I noticed there was a hole in the bottom of his pail.

"I strolled up. There was no hurry. You see the thing had gone off like a box of matches. It had been hopeless from the very first. The flame had leaped high, driven everybody back, lighted up everything—and collapsed. The shed was already a heap of embers glowing fiercely.

A nigger was being beaten near by. They said he had caused the fire in some way; be that as it may, he was screeching most horribly. I saw him, later, for several days, sitting in a bit of shade looking very sick and trying to recover himself: afterwards he arose and went out—and the wilderness without a sound took him into its bosom again. As I approached the glow from the dark I found myself at the back of two men, talking. I heard the name of Kurtz pronounced, then the words, 'take advantage of this unfortunate accident.' One of the men was the manager. I wished him a good evening. 'Did you ever see anything like it—eh? it is incredible,' he said, and walked off. The other man remained. He was a first-class agent, young, gentlemanly, a bit reserved, with a forked little beard and a hooked nose. He was stand-offish with the other agents, and they on their side said he was the manager's spy upon them. As to me, I had hardly ever spoken to him before. We got into talk, and by and by we strolled away from the hissing ruins. Then he asked me to his room, which was in the main building of the station. He struck a match, and I perceived that this young aristocrat had not only a silver-mounted dressing-case but also a whole candle all to himself. Just at that time the manager was the only man supposed to have any right to candles. Native mats covered the clay walls; a collection of spears, assegais, shields, knives, was hung up in trophies. The business entrusted to this fellow was the making of bricks—so I had been informed; but there wasn't a fragment of a brick anywhere in the station, and he had been there more than a year—waiting. It seems he could not make bricks without something, I don't know what—straw maybe. Anyway, it could not be found there, and as it was not likely to be sent from Europe, it did not appear clear to me what he was waiting for. An act of special creation perhaps. However, they were all waiting—all the sixteen or twenty pilgrims of them—for something; and upon my word it did not seem an uncongenial occupation, from the way they took it, though the only thing that ever came to them was disease—as far as I could see. They beguiled the time by backbiting and intriguing against each other in a foolish kind of way. There was an air of plotting about that station, but nothing came of it, of course. It was as unreal as everything else—as the philanthropic pretence of the whole concern, as their talk, as their government, as their show of work. The only real feeling was a desire to get appointed to a trading-post where ivory was to be had, so that they could earn percentages. They intrigued and slandered and hated each other only on that account—but as to effectually lifting a little finger—oh no. By heavens! there is something after all in the world allowing one man to steal a horse while another must not look at a halter. Steal a horse straight out. Very well. He has done it. Perhaps he can ride. But there is a way of looking at a halter that would provoke the most charitable of saints into a kick.

"I had no idea why he wanted to be sociable, but as we chatted in there it suddenly occurred to me the fellow was trying to get at something—in fact, pumping me. He alluded constantly to Europe, to the people I was supposed to know there—putting leading questions as to my acquaintances in the sepulchral city, and so on. His little eyes glittered like mica discs—with curiosity—though he tried to keep up a bit of superciliousness. At first I was astonished, but very soon I became awfully curious to see what he would find out from me. I couldn't possibly imagine what I had in me to make it worth his while. It was very pretty to see how he baffled himself, for in truth my body was full only of chills, and my head had nothing in it but that wretched steamboat business. It was evident he took me for a perfectly shameless prevaricator. At last he got angry, and, to conceal a movement of furious annoyance, he yawned. I rose. Then I noticed a small sketch in oils, on a panel, representing a woman, draped and blindfolded, carrying a lighted torch. The background was sombre—almost black. The movement of the woman was stately, and the effect of the torchlight on the face was sinister.

"It arrested me, and he stood by civilly, holding an empty half-pint champagne bottle (medical comforts) with the candle stuck in it. To my question he said Mr. Kurtz had painted this—in this very station more than a year ago—while waiting for means to go to his trading-post. 'Tell me, pray,' said I, 'who is this Mr. Kurtz?'

" 'The chief of the Inner Station,' he answered in a short tone, looking away. 'Much obliged,' I said, laughing. 'And you are the brickmaker of the Central Station. Every one knows that.' He was silent for a while. 'He is a prodigy,' he said at last. 'He is an emissary of pity, and science, and progress, and devil knows what else. We want,' he began to declaim suddenly, 'for the guidance of the cause entrusted to us by Europe, so to speak, higher intelligence, wide sympathies, a singleness of purpose.' 'Who says that?' I asked. 'Lots of them,' he replied. 'Some even write that; and so *he* comes here, a special being, as you ought to know.' 'Why ought I to know?' I interrupted, really surprised. He paid no attention. 'Yes. To-day he is chief of the best station, next year he will be assistant-manager, two years more and ... but I daresay you know what he will be in two years' time. You are of the new gang—the gang of virtue. The same people who sent him specially also recommended you. Oh, don't say no. I've my own eyes to trust.' Light dawned upon me. My dear aunt's influential acquaintances were producing an unexpected effect upon that young man. I nearly burst into a laugh. 'Do you read the Company's confidential correspondence?' I asked. He hadn't a word to say. It was great fun. 'When Mr. Kurtz,' I continued severely, 'is General Manager, you won't have the opportunity.'

"He blew the candle out suddenly, and we went outside. The moon had risen. Black figures strolled about listlessly, pouring water on the glow, whence proceeded a sound of hissing; steam ascended in the moonlight; the beaten nigger groaned somewhere. 'What a row the brute makes!' said the indefatigable man with the moustaches, appearing near us. 'Serve him right. Transgression—punishment—bang! Pitiless, pitiless. That's the only way. This will prevent all conflagrations for the future. I was just telling the manager ...' He noticed my companion, and became crestfallen all at once. 'Not in bed yet,' he said, with a kind of servile heartiness; 'it's so natural. Ha! Danger—agitation.' He vanished. I went on to the river-side, and the other followed me. I heard a scathing murmur at my ear, 'Heap of muffs—go to.' The pilgrims could be seen in knots gesticulating, discussing. Several had still their staves in their hands. I verily believe they took these sticks to bed with them. Beyond the fence the forest stood up spectrally in the moonlight, and through the dim stir, through the faint sounds of that lamentable courtyard, the silence of the land went home to one's very heart—its mystery, its greatness, the amazing reality of its concealed life. The hurt nigger moaned feebly somewhere near by, and then fetched a deep sigh that made me mend my pace away from there. I felt a hand introducing itself under my arm. 'My dear sir,' said the fellow, 'I don't want to be misunderstood, and especially by you, who will see Mr. Kurtz long before I can have that pleasure. I wouldn't like him to get a false idea of my disposition. . . .'

"I let him run on, this papier-mâché Mephistopheles, and it seemed to me that if I tried I could poke my forefinger through him, and would find nothing inside but a little loose dirt, maybe. He, don't you see, had been planning to be assistant-manager by and by under the present man, and I could see that the coming of that Kurtz had upset them both not a little. He talked precipitately, and I did not try to stop him. I had my shoulders against the wreck of my steamer, hauled up on the slope like a carcass of some big river animal. The smell of mud, of primeval mud, by Jove! was in my nostrils, the high stillness of primeval forest was before my eyes; there were shiny patches on the black creek. The moon had spread over everything a thin layer of silver—over the rank grass, over the mud, upon the wall of matted vegetation standing higher than the wall of a temple, over the great river I could see through a sombre gap glittering, glittering, as it flowed broadly by without a murmur. All this was great, expectant, mute, while the man jabbered about himself. I wondered whether the stillness on the face of the immensity looking at us two were meant as an appeal or as a menace. What were we who had strayed in here? Could we handle that dumb thing, or would it handle us? I felt how big, how confoundedly big, was that thing that couldn't talk and perhaps was deaf as well. What was in there? I could see a little ivory coming out from there, and I had heard Mr. Kurtz was in there. I had heard enough about it too—God knows! Yet somehow it didn't bring any image with it—no more than if I had been told an angel or a fiend was in there. I believed it in the same way one of you might believe there are inhabitants in the planet Mars. I knew once a Scotch sailmaker who was certain, dead sure, there were people in Mars. If you asked him for some idea how they looked and behaved, he would get shy and mutter something about 'walking on all-fours.' If you as much as smiled, he would—though a man of sixty—offer to fight you. I would not have gone so far as to fight for Kurtz, but I went for him near enough to a lie. You know I hate, detest, and can't bear a lie, not because I am straighter than the rest of us, but simply because it appals me. There is a taint of death, a flavour of mortality in lies—which is exactly what I hate and detest in the world—what I want to forget. It makes me miserable and sick, like biting something rotten would do. Temperament, I suppose. Well, I went near enough to it by letting the young fool there believe anything he liked to imagine as to my influence in Europe. I became in an instant as much of a pretence as the rest of the bewitched pilgrims. This simply because I had a notion it somehow would be of help to that Kurtz whom at the time I did not see—you understand. He was just a word for me. I did not see the man in the name any more than you do. Do you see him? Do you see the story? Do you see anything? It seems to me I am trying to tell you a dream—making a vain attempt, because no relation of a dream can convey the dream-sensation, that commingling of absurdity, surprise, and bewilderment in a tremor of struggling revolt, that notion of being captured by the incredible which is of the very essence of dreams. . . ."

He was silent for a while.

". . . No, it is impossible; it is impossible to convey the life-sensation of any given epoch of one's existence—that which makes its truth, its meaning—its subtle and penetrating essence. It is impossible. We live, as we dream—alone. . . ."

He paused again as if reflecting, then added:

"Of course in this you fellows see more than I could then. You see me, whom you know. . . ."

It had become so pitch dark that we listeners could hardly see one another. For a long time already he, sitting apart, had been no more to us than a voice. There was not a word from anybody. The others might have been asleep, but I was awake. I listened, I listened on the watch for the sentence, for the word, that would give me the clue to the faint uneasiness inspired by this narrative that seemed to shape itself without human lips in the heavy night-air of the river.

". . . Yes—I let him run on," Marlow began again, "and think what he pleased about the powers that were behind me. I did! And there was nothing behind me! There was nothing but that wretched, old, mangled steamboat I was leaning against, while he talked fluently about 'the necessity for every man to get on.' 'And when one comes out here, you conceive, it is not to gaze at the moon.' Mr. Kurtz was a 'universal genius,' but even a genius would find it easier to work with 'adequate tools—intelligent men.' He did not make bricks—why, there was a physical impossibility in the way—as I was well aware; and if he did secretarial work for the manager, it was because 'no sensible man rejects wantonly the confidence of his superiors.' Did I see it? I saw it. What more did I want? What I really wanted was rivets, by heaven! Rivets. To get on with the work—to stop the hole. Rivets I wanted. There were cases of them down at the coast—cases—piled up—burst—split! You kicked a loose rivet at every second step in that station yard on the hillside. Rivets had rolled into the grove of death. You could fill your pockets with rivets for the trouble of stooping down—and there wasn't one rivet to be found where it was wanted. We had plates that would do, but nothing to fasten them with. And every week the messenger, a lone negro, letter-bag on shoulder and staff in hand, left our station for the coast. And several times a week a coast caravan came in with trade goods—ghastly glazed calico that made you shudder only to look at it, glass beads value about a penny a quart, confounded spotted cotton handkerchiefs. And no rivets. Three carriers could have brought all that was wanted to set that steamboat afloat.

"He was becoming confidential now, but I fancy my unresponsive attitude must have exasperated him at last, for he judged it necessary to inform me he feared neither God nor devil, let alone any mere man. I said I could see that very well, but what I wanted was a certain quantity of rivets—and rivets were what really Mr. Kurtz wanted, if he had only known it. Now letters went to the coast every week. . . . 'My dear sir,' he cried, 'I write from dictation.' I demanded rivets. There was a way—for an intelligent man. He changed his manner; became very cold, and suddenly began to talk about a hippopotamus; wondered whether sleeping on board the steamer (I stuck to my salvage night and day) I wasn't disturbed. There was an old hippo that had the bad habit of getting out on the bank and roaming at night over the station grounds. The pilgrims used to turn out in a body and empty every rifle they could lay hands on at him. Some even had sat up o' nights for him. All this energy was wasted, though. 'That animal has a charmed life,' he said; 'but you can say this only of brutes in this country. No man—you apprehend me?—no man here bears a charmed life.' He stood there for a moment in the moonlight with his delicate hooked nose set a little askew, and his mica eyes glittering without a wink, then, with a curt Good-night, he strode off. I could see he was disturbed and considerably puzzled, which made me feel more hopeful than I had been for days. It was a great comfort to turn from that chap to my influential friend, the battered, twisted, ruined, tin-pot steamboat. I clambered on board. She rang under my feet like an empty Huntley & Palmer biscuit-tin kicked along a gutter; she was nothing so solid in make, and rather less pretty in shape, but I had expended enough hard work on her to make me love her. No influential friend would have served me better. She had given me a chance to come out a bit—to find out what I could do. No, I don't like work. I had rather laze about and think of all the fine things that can be done. I don't like work—no man does—but I like what is in the work—the chance to find yourself. Your own reality—for yourself, not for others—what no other man can ever know. They can only see the mere show, and never can tell what it really means.

"I was not surprised to see somebody sitting aft, on the deck, with his legs dangling over the mud. You see I rather chummed with the few mechanics there were in that station, whom the other pilgrims naturally despised—on account of their imperfect manners, I suppose. This was the foreman—a boiler-maker by trade—a good worker. He was a lank, bony, yellow-faced man, with big intense eyes. His aspect was worried, and his head was as bald as the palm of my hand; but his hair in falling seemed to have stuck to his chin, and had prospered in the new locality, for his beard hung down to his waist. He was a widower with six young children (he had left them in charge of a sister of his to come out there), and the passion of his life was pigeon-flying. He was an enthusiast and a connoisseur. He would rave about pigeons. After work hours he used sometimes to come over from his hut for a talk about his children and his pigeons; at work, when he had to crawl in the mud under the bottom of the steamboat, he would tie up that beard of his in a kind of white serviette he brought for the purpose. It had loops to go over his ears. In the evening he could be seen squatted on the bank rinsing that wrapper in the creek with great care, then spreading it solemnly on a bush to dry.

"I slapped him on the back and shouted 'We shall have rivets!' He scrambled to his feet exclaiming 'No! Rivets!' as though he couldn't believe his ears. Then in a low voice, 'You . . . eh?' I don't know why we behaved like lunatics. I put my finger to the side of my nose and nodded mysteriously. 'Good for you!' he cried, snapped his fingers above his head, lifting one foot. I tried a jig. We capered on the iron deck. A frightful clatter came out of that hulk, and the virgin forest on the other bank of the creek sent it back in a thundering roll upon the sleeping station. It must have made some of the pilgrims sit up in their hovels. A dark figure obscured the lighted doorway of the manager's hut, vanished, then, a second or so after, the doorway itself vanished too. We stopped, and the silence driven away by the stamping of our feet flowed back again from the recesses of the land. The great wall of vegetation, an exuberant and entangled mass of trunks, branches, leaves, boughs, festoons, motionless in the moonlight, was like a rioting invasion of soundless life, a rolling wave of plants, piled up, crested, ready to topple over the creek, to sweep every little man of us out of his little existence. And it moved not. A deadened burst of mighty splashes and snorts reached us from afar, as though an ichthyosaurus had been taking a bath of glitter in the great river.

'After all,' said the boiler-maker in a reasonable tone, 'why shouldn't we get the rivets?' Why not, indeed! I did not know of any reason why we shouldn't. 'They'll come in three weeks,'' I said confidently.

"But they didn't. Instead of rivets there came an invasion, an infliction, a visitation. It came in sections during the next three weeks, each section headed by a donkey carrying a white man in new clothes and tan shoes, bowing from that elevation right and left to the impressed pilgrims. A quarrelsome band of footsore sulky niggers trod on the heels of the donkey; a lot of tents, camp-stools, tin boxes, white cases, brown bales would be shot down in the courtyard, and the air of mystery would deepen a little over the muddle of the station. Five such instalments came, with their absurd air of disorderly flight with the loot of innumerable outfit shops and provision stores, that, one would think, they were lugging, after a raid, into the wilderness for equitable division. It was an inextricable mess of things decent in themselves but that human folly made look like the spoils of thieving.

"This devoted band called itself the Eldorado Exploring Expedition, and I believe they were sworn to secrecy. Their talk, however, was the talk of sordid buccaneers: it was reckless without hardihood, greedy without audacity, and cruel without courage; there was not an atom of foresight or of serious intention in the whole batch of them, and they did not seem aware these things are wanted for the work of the world. To tear treasure out of the bowels of the land was their desire, with no more moral purpose at the back of it than there is in burglars breaking into a safe. Who paid the expenses of the noble enterprise I don't know; but the uncle of our manager was leader of that lot.

"In exterior he resembled a butcher in a poor neighbourhood, and his eyes had a look of sleepy cunning. He carried his fat paunch with ostentation on his short legs, and during the time his gang infested the station spoke to no one but his nephew. You could see these two roaming about all day long with their heads close together in an everlasting confab.

"I had given up worrying myself about the rivets. One's capacity for that kind of folly is more limited than you would suppose. I said Hang!—and let things slide. I had plenty of time for meditation, and now and then I would give some thought to Kurtz. I wasn't very interested in him. No. Still, I was curious to see whether this man, who had come out equipped with moral ideas of some sort, would climb to the top after all, and how he would set about his work when there."

II

"One evening as I was lying flat on the deck of my steamboat, I heard voices approaching—and there were the nephew and the uncle strolling along the bank. I laid my head on my arm again, and had nearly lost myself in a doze, when somebody said in my ear, as it were: 'I am as harmless as a little child, but I don't like to be dictated to. Am I the manager—or am I not? I was ordered to send him there. It's incredible.' . . . I became aware that the two were standing on the shore alongside the forepart of the steamboat, just below my head. I did not move; it did not occur to me to move: I was sleepy. 'It *is* unpleasant,' grunted the uncle. 'He has asked the Administration to be sent there,' said the other, 'with the idea of showing what he could do; and I was instructed accordingly. Look at the influence that man must have. Is it not frightful?' They both agreed it was frightful, then made several bizarre remarks: 'Make rain and fine weather—one man—the Council—by the nose'—bits of absurd sentences that got the better of my drowsiness, so that I had pretty near the whole of my wits about me when the uncle said, 'The climate may do away with this difficulty for you. Is he alone there?' 'Yes,' answered the manager; 'he sent his assistant down the river with a note to me in these terms: "Clear this poor devil out of the country, and don't bother sending more of that sort. I had rather be alone than have the kind of men you can dispose of with me." It was more than a year ago. Can you imagine such impudence?' 'Anything since then?' asked the other hoarsely. 'Ivory,' jerked the nephew; 'lots of it—prime sort—lots—most annoying, from him.' 'And with that?' questioned the heavy rumble. 'Invoice,' was the reply fired out, so to speak. Then silence. They had been talking about Kurtz.

"I was broad awake by this time, but, lying perfectly at ease, remained still, having no inducement to change my position. 'How did that ivory come all this way?' growled the elder man, who seemed very vexed. The other explained that it had come with a fleet of canoes in charge of an English half-caste clerk Kurtz had with him; that Kurtz had apparently intended to return himself, the station being by that time bare of goods and stores, but after coming three hundred miles, had suddenly decided to go back, which he started to do alone in a small dugout with four paddlers, leaving the half-caste to continue down the river with the ivory. The two fellows there seemed astounded at anybody attempting such a thing. They were at a loss for an adequate motive. As for me, I seemed to see Kurtz for the first time. It was a distinct glimpse: the dugout, four paddling savages, and the lone white man turning his back suddenly on the headquarters, on relief, on thoughts of home—perhaps; setting his face towards the depths of the wilderness, towards his empty and desolate station. I did not know the motive. Perhaps he was just simply a fine fellow who stuck to his work for its own sake. His name, you understand, had not been pronounced once. He was 'that man.' The half-caste, who, as far as I could see, had conducted a difficult trip with great prudence and pluck, was invariably alluded to as 'that scoundrel.' The 'scoundrel' had reported that the 'man' had been very ill—had recovered imperfectly. . . . The two below me moved away then a few paces, and strolled back and forth at some little distance. I heard: 'Military post—doctor—two hundred miles—quite alone now—unavoidable delays—nine months—no news—strange rumours.' They approached again, just as the manager was saying, 'No one, as far as I know, unless a species of wandering trader—a pestilential fellow, snapping ivory from the natives.' Who was it they were talking about now? I gathered in snatches that this was some man supposed to be in Kurtz's district, and of whom the manager did not approve. 'We will not be free from unfair competition till one of these fellows is hanged for an example,' he said. 'Certainly,' grunted the other; 'get him hanged! Why not? Anything—anything can be done in this country. That's what I say; nobody here, you understand, *here,* can endanger your position. And why? You stand the climate—you outlast them all. The danger is in Europe; but there before I left I took care to—' They moved off and whispered, then their voices rose again. 'The extraordinary series of delays is not my fault. I did my possible.' The fat man sighed, 'Very sad.' 'And the pestiferous absurdity of his talk,' continued the other; 'he bothered me enough when he was here. "Each station should be like a beacon on the road towards better things, a centre for trade of course, but also for humanising, improving, instructing." Conceive you—that ass! And he wants to be manager! No, it's—' Here he got choked by excessive indignation, and I lifted my head the least bit. I was surprised to see how near they were—right under me. I could have spat upon their hats. They were looking on the ground, absorbed in thought. The manager was switching his leg with a slender twig: his sagacious relative lifted his head. 'You have been well since you came out this time?' he asked. The other gave a start. 'Who? I? Oh! Like a charm—like a charm. But the rest—oh, my goodness! All sick. They die so quick, too, that I haven't the time to send them out of the country—it's incredible!' 'H'm. Just so,' grunted the uncle. 'Ah! my boy, trust to this—I say, trust to this.' I saw him extend his short flipper of an arm for a gesture that took in the forest, the creek, the mud, the river—seemed to beckon with a dishonouring flourish before the sunlit face of the land a treacherous appeal to the lurking death, to the hidden evil, to the profound darkness of its heart. It was so startling that I leaped to my feet and looked back at the edge of the forest, as though I had expected an answer of some sort to that black display of confidence. You know the foolish notions that come to one sometimes. The high stillness confronted these two figures with its ominous patience, waiting for the passing away of a fantastic invasion.

"They swore aloud together—out of sheer fright, I believe—then, pretending not to know anything of my existence, turned back to the station. The sun was low; and leaning forward side by side, they seemed to be tugging painfully uphill their two ridiculous shadows of unequal length, that trailed behind them slowly over the tall grass without bending a single blade.

"In a few days the Eldorado Expedition went into the patient wilderness, that closed upon it as the sea closes over a diver. Long afterwards the news came that all the donkeys were dead. I know nothing as to the fate of the less valuable animals. They, no doubt, like the rest of us, found what they deserved. I did not inquire. I was then rather excited at the prospect of meeting Kurtz very soon. When I say very soon I mean it comparatively. It was just two months from the day we left the creek when we came to the bank below Kurtz's station.

"Going up that river was like travelling back to the earliest beginnings of the world, when vegetation rioted on the earth and the big trees were kings. An empty stream, a great silence, an impenetrable forest. The air was warm, thick, heavy, sluggish. There was no joy in the brilliance of sunshine. The long stretches of the waterway ran on, deserted, into the gloom of overshadowed distances. On silvery sandbanks hippos and alligators sunned themselves side by side. The broadening waters flowed through a mob of wooded islands; you lost your way on that river as you would in a desert, and butted all day long against shoals, trying to find the channel, till you thought yourself bewitched and cut off for ever from everything you had known once—somewhere—far away—in another existence perhaps. There were moments when one's past came back to one, as it will sometimes when you have not a moment to spare to yourself; but it came in the shape of an unrestful and noisy dream, remembered with wonder amongst the overwhelming realities of this strange world of plants, and water, and silence. And this stillness of life did not in the least resemble a peace. It was the stillness of an implacable force brooding over an inscrutable intention. It looked at you with a vengeful aspect. I got used to it afterwards; I did not see it any more; I had no time. I had to keep guessing at the channel; I had to discern, mostly by inspiration, the signs of hidden banks; I watched for sunken stones; I was learning to clap my teeth smartly before my heart flew out, when I shaved by a fluke some infernal sly old snag that would have ripped the life out of the tin-pot steamboat and drowned all the pilgrims; I had to keep a look-out for the signs of dead wood we could cut up in the night for next day's steaming. When you have to attend to things of that sort, to the mere incidents of the surface, the reality—the reality, I tell you—fades. The inner truth is hidden—luckily, luckily. But I felt it all the same; I felt often its mysterious stillness watching me at my monkey tricks, just as it watches you fellows performing on your respective tight-ropes for—what is it? half a crown a tumble—"

"Try to be civil, Marlow," growled a voice, and I knew there was at least one listener awake besides myself.

"I beg your pardon. I forgot the heartache which makes up the rest of the price. And indeed what does the price matter, if the trick be well done? You do your tricks very well. And I didn't do badly either, since I managed not to sink that steamboat on my first trip. It's a wonder to me yet. Imagine a blindfolded man set to drive a van over a bad road. I sweated and shivered over that business considerably, I can tell you. After all, for a seaman, to scrape the bottom of the thing that's supposed to float all the time under his care is the unpardonable sin. No one may know of it, but you never forget the thump—eh? A blow on the very heart. You remember it, you dream of it, you wake up at night and think of it—years after—and go hot and cold all over. I don't pretend to say that steamboat floated all the time. More than once she had to wade for a bit, with twenty cannibals splashing around and pushing. We had enlisted some of these chaps on the way for a crew. Fine fellows—cannibals—in their place. They were men one could work with, and I am grateful to them. And, after all, they did not eat each other before my face: they had brought along a provision of hippo-meat which went rotten, and made the mystery of the wilderness stink in my nostrils. Phoo! I can sniff it now. I had the manager on board and three or four pilgrims with their staves—all complete. Sometimes we came upon a station close by the bank, clinging to the skirts of the unknown, and the white men rushing out of a tumble-down hovel, with great gestures of joy and surprise and welcome, seemed very strange—had the appearance of being held there captive by a spell. The word 'ivory' would ring in the air for a while—and on we went again into the silence, along empty reaches, round the still bends, between the high walls of our winding way, reverberating in hollow claps the ponderous beat of the stern-wheel. Trees, trees, millions of trees, massive, immense, running up high; and at their foot, hugging the bank against the stream, crept the little begrimed steamboat, like a sluggish beetle crawling on the floor of a lofty portico. It made you feel very small, very lost, and yet it was not altogether depressing, that feeling. After all, if you were small, the grimy beetle crawled on—which was just what you wanted it to do. Where the pilgrims imagined it crawled to I don't know. To some place where they expected to get something, I bet! For me it crawled towards Kurtz—exclusively; but when the steam-pipes started leaking we crawled very slow. The reaches opened before us and closed behind, as if the forest had stepped leisurely across the water to bar the way for our return. We penetrated deeper and deeper into the heart of darkness. It was very quiet there. At night sometimes the roll of drums behind the curtain of trees would run up the river and remain sustained faintly, as if hovering in the air high over our heads, till the first break of day. Whether it meant war, peace, or prayer we could not tell. The dawns were heralded by the descent of a chill stillness; the woodcutters slept, their fires burned low; the snapping of a twig would make you start. We were wanderers on a prehistoric earth, on an earth that wore the aspect of an unknown planet. We could have fancied ourselves the first of men taking possession of an accursed inheritance, to be subdued at the cost of profound anguish and of excessive toil. But suddenly, as we struggled round a bend, there would be a glimpse of rush walls, of peaked grass-roofs, a burst of yells, a whirl of black limbs, a mass of hands clapping, of feet stamping, of bodies swaying, of eyes rolling, under the droop of heavy and motionless foliage. The steamer toiled along slowly on the edge of a black and incomprehensible frenzy. The prehistoric man was cursing us, praying to us, welcoming us—who could tell? We were cut off from the comprehension of our surroundings; we glided past like phantoms, wondering and secretly appalled, as sane men would be before an enthusiastic outbreak in a madhouse. We could not understand because we were too far and could not remember, because we were travelling in the night of first ages, of those ages that are gone, leaving hardly a sign—and no memories.

"The earth seemed unearthly. We are accustomed to look upon the shackled form of a conquered monster, but there—there you could look at a thing monstrous and free. It was unearthly, and the men were— No, they were not inhuman. Well, you know, that was the worst of it—this suspicion of their not being inhuman. It would come slowly to one. They howled and leaped, and spun, and made horrid faces; but what thrilled you was just the thought of their humanity—like yours—the thought of your remote kinship with this wild and passionate uproar. Ugly. Yes, it was ugly enough; but if you were man enough you would admit to yourself that there was in you just the faintest trace of a response to the terrible frankness of that noise, a dim suspicion of there being a meaning in it which you—you so remote from the night of first ages—could comprehend. And why not? The mind of man is capable of anything—because everything is in it, all the past as well as all the future. What was there after all? Joy, fear, sorrow, devotion, valour, rage—who can tell?—but truth—truth stripped of its cloak of time. Let the fool gape and shudder—the man knows, and can look on without a wink. But he must at least be as much of a man as these on the shore. He must meet that truth with his own true stuff—with his own inborn strength. Principles? Principles won't do. Acquisitions, clothes, pretty rags—rags that would fly off at the first good shake. No; you want a deliberate belief. An appeal to me in this fiendish row—is there? Very well; I hear; I admit, but I have a voice too, and for good or evil mine is the speech that cannot be silenced. Of course, a fool, what with sheer fright and fine sentiments, is always safe. Who's that grunting? You wonder I didn't go ashore for a howl and a dance? Well, no—I didn't. Fine sentiments, you say? Fine sentiments be hanged! I had no time. I had to mess about with white-lead and strips of woollen blanket helping to put bandages on those leaky steam-pipes—I tell you. I had to watch the steering, and circumvent those snags, and get the tin-pot along by hook or by crook. There was surface-truth enough in these things to save a wiser man. And between whiles I had to look after the savage who was fireman. He was an improved specimen; he could fire up a vertical boiler. He was there below me, and, upon my word, to look at him was as edifying as seeing a dog in a parody of breeches and a feather hat, walking on his hind legs. A few months of training had done for that really fine chap. He squinted at the steam-gauge and at the water-gauge with an evident effort of intrepidity—and he had filed teeth too, the poor devil, and the wool of his pate shaved into queer patterns, and three ornamental scars on each of his cheeks. He ought to have been clapping his hands and stamping his feet on the bank, instead of which he was hard at work, a thrall to strange witchcraft, full of improving knowledge. He was useful because he had been instructed; and what he knew was this—that should the water in that transparent thing disappear, the evil spirit inside the boiler would get angry through the greatness of his thirst, and take a terrible vengeance. So he sweated and fired up and watched the glass fearfully (with an impromptu charm, made of rags, tied to his arm, and a piece of polished bone, as big as a watch, stuck flatways through his lower lip), while the wooded banks slipped past us slowly, the short noise was left behind, the interminable miles of silence—and we crept on, towards Kurtz. But the snags were thick, the water was treacherous and shallow, the boiler seemed indeed to have a sulky devil in it, and thus neither that fireman nor I had any time to peer into our creepy thoughts.

"Some fifty miles below the Inner Station we came upon a hut of reeds, an inclined and melancholy pole, with the unrecognisable tatters of what had been a flag of some sort flying from it, and a neatly stacked wood-pile. This was unexpected. We came to the bank, and on the stack of firewood found a flat piece of board with some faded pencil-writing on it. When deciphered it said: 'Wood for you. Hurry up. Approach cautiously.' There was a signature, but it was illegible—not Kurtz—a much longer word. Hurry up. Where? Up the river? 'Approach cautiously.' We had not done so. But the warning could not have been meant for the place where it could be only found after approach. Something was wrong above. But what—and how much? That was the question. We commented adversely upon the imbecility of that telegraphic style. The bush around said nothing, and would not let us look very far, either. A torn curtain of red twill hung in the doorway of the hut, and flapped sadly in our faces. The dwelling was dismantled; but we could see a white man had lived there not very long ago. There remained a rude table—a plank on two posts; a heap of rubbish reposed in a dark corner, and by the door I picked up a book. It had lost its covers, and the pages had been thumbed into a state of extremely dirty softness; but the back had been lovingly stitched afresh with white cotton thread, which looked clean yet. It was an extraordinary find. Its title was, *An Inquiry into some Points of Seamanship,* by a man Towser, Towson—some such name—Master in

His Majesty's Navy. The matter looked dreary reading enough, with illustrative diagrams and repulsive tables of figures, and the copy was sixty years old. I handled this amazing antiquity with the greatest possible tenderness, lest it should dissolve in my hands. Within, Towson or Towser was inquiring earnestly into the breaking strain of ships' chains and tackle, and other such matters. Not a very enthralling book; but at the first glance you could see there a singleness of intention, an honest concern for the right way of going to work, which made these humble pages, thought out so many years ago, luminous with another than a professional light. The simple old sailor, with his talk of chains and purchases, made me forget the jungle and the pilgrims in a delicious sensation of having come upon something unmistakably real. Such a book being there was wonderful enough; but still more astounding were the notes pencilled in the margin, and plainly referring to the text. I couldn't believe my eyes! They were in cipher! Yes, it looked like cipher. Fancy a man lugging with him a book of that description into this nowhere and studying it—and making notes—in cipher at that! It was an extravagant mystery.

"I had been dimly aware for some time of a worrying noise, and when I lifted my eyes I saw the wood-pile was gone, and the manager, aided by all the pilgrims, was shouting at me from the river-side. I slipped the book into my pocket. I assure you to leave off reading was like tearing myself away from the shelter of an old and solid friendship.

"I started the lame engine ahead. 'It must be this miserable trader—this intruder,' exclaimed the manager, looking back malevolently at the place we had left. 'He must be English,' I said. 'It will not save him from getting into trouble if he is not careful,' muttered the manager darkly. I observed with assumed innocence that no man was safe from trouble in this world.

"The current was more rapid now, the steamer seemed at her last gasp, the stern-wheel flopped languidly, and I caught myself listening on tiptoe for the next beat of the float, for in sober truth I expected the wretched thing to give up every moment. It was like watching the last flickers of a life. But still we crawled. Sometimes I would pick out a tree a little way ahead to measure our progress towards Kurtz by, but I lost it invariably before we got abreast. To keep the eyes so long on one thing was too much for human patience. The manager displayed a beautiful resignation. I fretted and fumed and took to arguing with myself whether or no I would talk openly with Kurtz; but before I could come to any conclusion it occurred to me that my speech or my silence, indeed any action of mine, would be a mere futility. What did it matter what any one knew or ignored? What did it matter who was manager? One gets sometimes such a flash of insight. The essentials of this affair lay deep under the surface, beyond my reach, and beyond my power of meddling.

"Towards the evening of the second day we judged ourselves about eight miles from Kurtz's station. I wanted to push on; but the manager looked grave, and told me the navigation up there was so dangerous that it would be advisable, the sun being very low already, to wait where we were till next morning. Moreover, he pointed out that if the warning to approach cautiously were to be followed, we must approach in daylight—not at dusk, or in the dark. This was sensible enough. Eight miles meant nearly three hours' steaming for us, and I could also see suspicious ripples at the upper end of the reach. Nevertheless, I was annoyed beyond expression at the delay, and most unreasonably too, since one night more could not matter much after so many months. As we had plenty of wood, and caution was the word, I brought up in the middle of the stream. The reach was narrow, straight, with high sides like a railway cutting. The dusk came gliding into it long before the sun had set. The current ran smooth and swift, but a dumb immobility sat on the banks. The living trees, lashed together by the creepers and every living bush of the undergrowth, might have been changed into stone, even to the slenderest twig, to the lightest leaf. It was not sleep—it seemed unnatural, like a state of trance. Not the faintest sound of any kind could be heard. You looked on amazed, and began to suspect yourself of being deaf—then the night came suddenly, and struck you blind as well. About three in the morning some large fish leaped, and the loud splash made me jump as though a gun had been fired. When the sun rose there was a white fog, very warm and clammy, and more blinding than the night. It did not shift or drive; it was just there, standing all round you like something solid. At eight or nine, perhaps, it lifted as a shutter lifts. We had a glimpse of the towering multitude of trees, of the immense matted jungle, with the blazing little ball of the sun hanging over it—all perfectly still—and then the white shutter came down again, smoothly, as if sliding in greased grooves. I ordered the chain, which we had begun to heave in, to be paid out again. Before it stopped running with a muffled rattle, a cry, a very loud cry, as of infinite desolation, soared slowly in the opaque air. It ceased. A complaining clamour, modulated in savage discords, filled our ears. The sheer unexpectedness of it made my hair stir under my cap. I don't know how it struck the others: to me it seemed as though the mist itself had screamed, so suddenly, and apparently from all sides at once, did this tumultuous and mournful uproar arise. It culminated in a hurried outbreak of almost intolerably excessive shrieking, which stopped short, leaving us stiffened in a variety of silly attitudes, and obstinately listening to the nearly as appalling and excessive silence. 'Good God! What is the meaning—?' stammered at my elbow one of the pilgrims—a little fat man, with sandy hair and red whiskers, who wore side-spring boots, and pink pyjamas tucked into his socks. Two others remained open-mouthed a whole minute, then dashed into the little cabin, to rush out incontinently and stand darting scared glances, with Winchesters at 'ready' in their hands. What we could see was just the steamer we were on, her outlines blurred as though she had been on the point of dissolving, and a misty strip of water, perhaps two feet broad, around her—and that was all. The rest of the world was nowhere, as far as our eyes and ears were concerned. Just nowhere. Gone, disappeared; swept off without leaving a whisper or a shadow behind.

"I went forward, and ordered the chain to be hauled in short, so as to be ready to trip the anchor and move the steamboat at once if necessary. 'Will they attack?' whispered an awed voice. 'We will all be butchered in this fog,' murmured another. The faces twitched with the strain, the hands trembled slightly, the eyes forgot to wink. It was very curious to see the contrast of expressions of the white men and of the black fellows of our crew, who were as much strangers to that part of the river as we, though their homes were only eight hundred miles away. The whites, of course greatly discomposed, had besides a curious look of being painfully shocked by such an outrageous row. The others had an alert, naturally interested expression; but their faces were essentially quiet, even those of the one or two who grinned as they hauled at the chain. Several exchanged short, grunting phrases, which seemed to settle the matter to their satisfaction. Their headman, a young, broad-chested black, severely draped in dark-blue fringed cloths, with fierce nostrils and his hair all done up artfully in oily ringlets, stood near me. 'Aha!' I said, just for good fellowship's sake. 'Catch 'im,' he snapped, with a bloodshot widening of his eyes and a flash of sharp teeth—'catch 'im. Give 'im to us.' 'To you, eh?' I asked; 'what would you do with them?' 'Eat 'im!' he said curtly, and, leaning his elbow on the rail, looked out into the fog in a dignified and profoundly pensive attitude. I would no doubt have been properly horrified, had it not occurred to me that he and his chaps must be very hungry: that they must have been growing increasingly hungry for at least this month past. They had been engaged for six months (I don't think a single one of them had any clear idea of time, as we at the end of countless ages have. They still belonged to the beginnings of time—had no inherited experience to teach them, as it were), and of course, as long as there was a piece of paper written over in accordance with some farcical law or other made down the river, it didn't enter anybody's head to trouble how they would live. Certainly they had brought with them some rotten hippo-meat, which couldn't have lasted very long, anyway, even if the pilgrims hadn't, in the midst of a shocking hullabaloo, thrown a considerable quantity of it overboard. It looked like a high-handed proceeding; but it was really a case of legitimate self-defence. You can't breathe dead hippo waking, sleeping, and eating, and at the same time keep your precarious grip on existence. Besides that, they had given them every week three pieces of brass wire, each about nine inches long; and the theory was they were to buy their provisions with that currency in river-side villages. You can see how *that* worked. There were either no villages, or the people were hostile, or the director, who like the rest of us fed out of tins, with an occasional old he-goat thrown in, didn't want to stop the steamer for some more or less recondite reasons. So, unless they swallowed the wire itself, or made loops of it to snare the fishes with, I don't see what good their extravagant salary could be to them. I must say it was paid with a regularity worthy of a large and honourable trading company. For the rest, the only thing to eat—though it didn't look eatable in the least—I saw in their possession was a few lumps of some stuff like half-cooked dough, of a dirty lavender colour, they kept wrapped in leaves, and now and then swallowed a piece of, but so small that it seemed done more for the look of the thing than for any serious purpose of sustenance. Why in the name of all the gnawing devils of hunger they didn't go for us—they were thirty to five—and have a good tuck-in for once, amazes me now when I think of it. They were big powerful men, with not much capacity to weigh the consequences, with courage, with strength, even yet, though their skins were no longer glossy and their muscles no longer hard. And I saw that something restraining, one of those human secrets that baffle probability, had come into play there. I looked at them with a swift quickening of interest—not because it occurred to me I might be eaten by them before very long, though I own to you that just then I perceived—in a new light, as it were—how unwholesome the pilgrims looked, and I hoped, yes, I positively hoped, that my aspect was not so—what shall I say?—so—unappetising: a touch of fantastic vanity which fitted well with the dream-sensation that pervaded all my days at that time. Perhaps I had a little fever too. One can't live with one's finger everlastingly on one's pulse. I had often 'a little fever,' or a little touch of other things—the playful paw-strokes of the wilderness, the preliminary trifling before the more serious onslaught which came in due course. Yes; I looked at them as you would on any human being, with a curiosity of their impulses, motives, capacities, weaknesses, when brought to the test of an inexorable physical necessity. Restraint! What possible restraint? Was it superstition, disgust, patience, fear—or some kind of primitive honour? No fear can stand up to hunger, no patience can wear it out, disgust simply does not exist where hunger is; and as to superstition, beliefs, and what you may call principles, they are less than chaff in a breeze. Don't you know the devilry of lingering starvation, its exasperating torment, its black thoughts, its sombre and brooding ferocity? Well, I do. It takes a man all his inborn strength to fight hunger properly. It's really easier to face bereavement, dishonour, and the perdition of one's soul—than this kind of prolonged hunger. Sad, but true. And these chaps too had no earthly reason for any kind of scruple. Restraint! I would just as soon have expected restraint from a hyena prowling amongst the corpses of a battlefield. But there was the fact facing me—the fact dazzling, to be seen, like the foam on the depths of the sea, like a ripple on an unfathomable enigma, a mystery greater—when I thought of it—than the curious, inexplicable note of desperate grief in this savage clamour that had swept by us on the river-bank, behind the blind whiteness of the fog.

"Two pilgrims were quarrelling in hurried whispers as to which bank. 'Left.' 'No, no; how can you? Right, right, of course.' 'It is very serious,' said the manager's voice behind me; 'I would be desolated if anything should happen to Mr. Kurtz before we came up.' I looked at him, and had not the slightest doubt he was sincere. He was just the kind of man who would wish to preserve appearances. That was his restraint. But when he muttered something about going on at once, I did not even take the trouble to answer him. I knew, and he knew, that it was impossible. Were we to let go our hold of the bottom, we would be absolutely in the air—in space. We wouldn't be able to tell where we were going to—whether up or down stream, or across—till we fetched against one bank or the other—and then we wouldn't know at first which it was. Of course I made no move. I had no mind for a smash-up. You couldn't imagine a more deadly place for a shipwreck. Whether drowned at once or not, we were sure to perish speedily in one way or another. 'I authorise you to take all the risks,' he said, after a short silence. 'I refuse to take any,' I said shortly; which was just the answer he expected, though its tone might have surprised him. 'Well, I must defer to your judgment. You are captain,' he said, with marked civility. I turned my shoulder to him in sign of my appreciation, and looked into the fog. How long would it last? It was the most hopeless look-out. The approach to this Kurtz grubbing for ivory in the wretched bush was beset by as many dangers as though he had been an enchanted princess sleeping in a fabulous castle. 'Will they attack, do you think?' asked the manager, in a confidential tone.

"I did not think they would attack, for several obvious reasons. The thick fog was one. If they left the bank in their canoes they would get lost in it, as we would be if we attempted to move. Still, I had also judged the jungle of both banks quite impenetrable—and yet eyes were in it, eyes that had seen us. The river-side bushes were certainly very thick; but the undergrowth behind was evidently penetrable. However, during the short lift I had seen no canoes anywhere in the reach—certainly not abreast of the steamer. But what made the idea of attack inconceivable to me was the nature of the noise—of the cries we had heard. They had not the fierce character boding of immediate hostile intention. Unexpected, wild, and violent as they had been, they had given me an irresistible impression of sorrow. The glimpse of the steamboat had for some reason filled those savages with unrestrained grief. The danger, if any, I expounded, was from our proximity to a great human passion let loose. Even extreme grief may ultimately vent itself in violence—but more generally takes the form of apathy....

"You should have seen the pilgrims stare! They had no heart to grin, or even to revile me; but I believe they thought me gone mad—with fright, maybe. I delivered a regular lecture. My dear boys, it was no good bothering. Keep a look-out? Well, you may guess I watched the fog for the signs of lifting as a cat watches a mouse; but for anything else our eyes were of no more use to us than if we had been buried miles deep in a heap of cotton-wool. It felt like it too—choking, warm, stifling. Besides, all I said, though it sounded extravagant, was absolutely true to fact. What we afterwards alluded to as an attack was really an attempt at repulse. The action was very far from being aggressive—it was not even defensive, in the usual sense: it was undertaken under the stress of desperation, and in its essence was purely protective.

"It developed itself, I should say, two hours after the fog lifted, and its commencement was at a spot, roughly speaking, about a mile and a half below Kurtz's station. We had just floundered and flopped round a bend, when I saw an islet, a mere grassy hummock of bright green, in the middle of the stream. It was the only thing of the kind; but as we opened the reach more, I perceived it was the head of a long sandbank, or rather of a chain of shallow patches stretching down the middle of the river. They were discoloured, just awash, and the whole lot was seen just under the water, exactly as a man's backbone is seen running down the middle of his back under the skin. Now, as far as I did see, I could go to the right or to the left of this. I didn't know either channel, of course. The banks looked pretty well alike, the depth appeared the same; but as I had been informed the station was on the west side, I naturally headed for the western passage.

"No sooner had we fairly entered it than I became aware it was much narrower than I had supposed. To the left of us there was the long uninterrupted shoal, and to the right a high steep bank heavily overgrown with bushes. Above the bush the trees stood in serried ranks. The twigs overhung the current thickly, and from distance to distance a large limb of some tree projected rigidly over the stream. It was then well on in the afternoon, the face of the forest was gloomy, and a broad strip of shadow had already fallen on the water. In this shadow we steamed up—very slowly, as you may imagine. I sheered her well inshore—the water being deepest near the bank, as the sounding-pole informed me.

"One of my hungry and forbearing friends was sounding in the bows just below me. This steamboat was exactly like a decked scow. On the deck there were two little teak-wood houses, with doors and windows. The boiler was in the fore-end, and the machinery right astern. Over the whole there was a light roof, supported on stanchions.

The funnel projected through that roof, and in front of the funnel a small cabin built of light planks served for a pilot-house. It contained a couch, two camp-stools, a loaded Martini-Henry leaning in one corner, a tiny table, and the steering-wheel. It had a wide door in front and a broad shutter at each side. All these were always thrown open, of course. I spent my days perched up there on the extreme fore-end of that roof, before the door. At night I slept, or tried to, on the couch. An athletic black belonging to some coast tribe, and educated by my poor predecessor, was the helmsman. He sported a pair of brass earrings, wore a blue cloth wrapper from the waist to the ankles, and thought all the world of himself. He was the most unstable kind of fool I had ever seen. He steered with no end of a swagger while you were by; but if he lost sight of you, he became instantly the prey of an abject funk, and would let that cripple of a steamboat get the upper hand of him in a minute.

"I was looking down at the sounding-pole, and feeling much annoyed to see at each try a little more of it stick out of that river, when I saw my poleman give up the business suddenly, and stretch himself flat on the deck, without even taking the trouble to haul his pole in. He kept hold on it though, and it trailed in the water. At the same time the fireman, whom I could also see below me, sat down abruptly before his furnace and ducked his head. I was amazed. Then I had to look at the river mighty quick, because there was a snag in the fairway. Sticks, little sticks, were flying about—thick: they were whizzing before my nose, dropping below me, striking behind me against my pilot-house. All this time the river, the shore, the woods, were very quiet—perfectly quiet. I could only hear the heavy splashing thump of the stern-wheel and the patter of these things. We cleared the snag clumsily. Arrows, by Jove! We were being shot at! I stepped in quickly to close the shutter on the land-side. That fool-helmsman, his hands on the spokes, was lifting his knees high, stamping his feet, champing his mouth, like a reined-in horse. Confound him! And we were staggering within ten feet of the bank. I had to lean right out to swing the heavy shutter, and I saw a face amongst the leaves on the level with my own, looking at me very fierce and steady; and then suddenly, as though a veil had been removed from my eyes, I made out, deep in the tangled gloom, naked breasts, arms, legs, glaring eyes—the bush was swarming with human limbs in movement, glistening, of bronze colour. The twigs shook, swayed, and rustled, the arrows flew out of them, and then the shutter came to. 'Steer her straight,' I said to the helmsman. He held his head rigid, face forward; but his eyes rolled, he kept on lifting and setting down his feet gently, his mouth foamed a little. 'Keep quiet!' I said in a fury. I might just as well have ordered a tree not to sway in the wind. I darted out. Below me there was a great scuffle of feet on the iron deck; confused exclamations; a voice screamed, 'Can you turn back?' I caught sight of a

V-shaped ripple on the water ahead. What? Another snag! A fusillade burst out under my feet. The pilgrims had opened with their Winchesters, and were simply squirting lead into that bush. A deuce of a lot of smoke came up and drove slowly forward. I swore at it. Now I couldn't see the ripple or the snag either. I stood in the doorway, peering, and the arrows came in swarms. They might have been poisoned, but they looked as though they wouldn't kill a cat. The bush began to howl. Our wood-cutters raised a warlike whoop; the report of a rifle just at my back deafened me. I glanced over my shoulder, and the pilot-house was yet full of noise and smoke when I made a dash at the wheel. The fool-nigger had dropped everything, to throw the shutter open and let off that Martini-Henry. He stood before the wide opening, glaring, and I yelled at him to come back, while I straightened the sudden twist out of that steamboat. There was no room to turn even if I had wanted to, the snag was somewhere very near ahead in that confounded smoke, there was no time to lose, so I just crowded her into the bank—right into the bank, where I knew the water was deep.

"We tore slowly along the overhanging bushes in a whirl of broken twigs and flying leaves. The fusillade below stopped short, as I had foreseen it would when the squirts got empty. I threw my head back to a glinting whizz that traversed the pilot-house, in at one shutter-hole and out at the other. Looking past that mad helmsman, who was shaking the empty rifle and yelling at the shore, I saw vague forms of men running bent double, leaping, gliding, distinct, incomplete, evanescent. Something big appeared in the air before the shutter, the rifle went overboard, and the man stepped back swiftly, looked at me over his shoulder in an extraordinary, profound, familiar manner, and fell upon my feet. The side of his head hit the wheel twice, and the end of what appeared a long cane clattered round and knocked over a little camp-stool. It looked as though after wrenching that thing from somebody ashore he had lost his balance in the effort. The thin smoke had blown away, we were clear of the snag, and looking ahead I could see that in another hundred yards or so I would be free to sheer off, away from the bank; but my feet felt so very warm and wet that I had to look down. The man had rolled on his back and stared straight up at me; both his hands clutched that cane. It was the shaft of a spear that, either thrown or lunged through the opening, had caught him in the side just below the ribs; the blade had gone in out of sight, after making a frightful gash; my shoes were full; a pool of blood lay very still, gleaming dark-red under the wheel; his eyes shone with an amazing lustre. The fusillade burst out again. He looked at me anxiously, gripping the spear like something precious, with an air of being afraid I would try to take it away from him. I had to make an effort to free my eyes from his gaze and attend to the steering. With one hand I felt above my head for the line of the steam whistle, and jerked out screech after screech hurriedly. The tumult of

angry and warlike yells was checked instantly, and then from the depths of the woods went out such a tremulous and prolonged wail of mournful fear and utter despair as may be imagined to follow the flight of the last hope from the earth. There was a great commotion in the bush; the shower of arrows stopped, a few dropping shots rang out sharply—then silence, in which the languid beat of the stern-wheel came plainly to my ears. I put the helm hard a-starboard at the moment when the pilgrim in pink pyjamas, very hot and agitated, appeared in the doorway. 'The manager sends me—' he began in an official tone, and stopped short. 'Good God!' he said, glaring at the wounded man.

"We two whites stood over him, and his lustrous and inquiring glance enveloped us both. I declare it looked as though he would presently put to us some question in an understandable language; but he died without uttering a sound, without moving a limb, without twitching a muscle. Only in the very last moment, as though in response to some sign we could not see, to some whisper we could not hear, he frowned heavily, and that frown gave to his black death-mask an inconceivably sombre, brooding, and menacing expression. The lustre of inquiring glance faded swiftly into vacant glassiness. 'Can you steer?' I asked the agent eagerly. He looked very dubious; but I made a grab at his arm, and he understood at once I meant him to steer whether or no. To tell you the truth, I was morbidly anxious to change my shoes and socks. 'He is dead,' murmured the fellow, immensely impressed. 'No doubt about it,' said I, tugging like mad at the shoe-laces. 'And by the way, I suppose Mr. Kurtz is dead as well by this time.'

"For the moment that was the dominant thought. There was a sense of extreme disappointment, as though I had found out I had been striving after something altogether without a substance. I couldn't have been more disgusted if I had travelled all this way for the sole purpose of talking with Mr. Kurtz. Talking with . . . I flung one shoe overboard, and became aware that that was exactly what I had been looking forward to—a talk with Kurtz. I made the strange discovery that I had never imagined him as doing, you know, but as discoursing. I didn't say to myself, 'Now I will never see him,' or 'Now I will never shake him by the hand,' but, 'Now I will never hear him.' The man presented himself as a voice. Not of course that I did not connect him with some sort of action. Hadn't I been told in all the tones of jealousy and admiration that he had collected, bartered, swindled, or stolen more ivory than all the other agents together? That was not the point. The point was in his being a gifted creature, and that of all his gifts the one that stood out pre-eminently, that carried with it a sense of real presence, was his ability to talk, his words—the gift of expression, the bewildering, the illuminating, the most exalted and the most contemptible, the pulsating stream of light, or the deceitful flow from the heart of an impenetrable darkness.

"The other shoe went flying unto the devil-god of that river. I thought, By Jove! it's all over. We are too late; he has vanished—the gift has vanished, by means of some spear, arrow, or club. I will never hear that chap speak after all—and my sorrow had a startling extravagance of emotion, even such as I had noticed in the howling sorrow of these savages in the bush. I couldn't have felt more of lonely desolation somehow, had I been robbed of a belief or had missed my destiny in life.... Why do you sigh in this beastly way, somebody? Absurd? Well, absurd. Good Lord! mustn't a man ever— Here, give me some tobacco." ...

There was a pause of profound stillness, then a match flared, and Marlow's lean face appeared, worn, hollow, with downward folds and dropped eyelids, with an aspect of concentrated attention; and as he took vigorous draws at his pipe, it seemed to retreat and advance out of the night in the regular flicker of the tiny flame. The match went out.

"Absurd!" he cried. "This is the worst of trying to tell ... Here you all are, each moored with two good addresses, like a hulk with two anchors, a butcher round one corner, a policeman round another, excellent appetites, and temperature normal—you hear—normal from year's end to year's end. And you say, Absurd! Absurd be—exploded! Absurd! My dear boys, what can you expect from a man who out of sheer nervousness had just flung overboard a pair of new shoes? Now I think of it, it is amazing I did not shed tears. I am, upon the whole, proud of my fortitude. I was cut to the quick at the idea of having lost the inestimable privilege of listening to the gifted Kurtz. Of course I was wrong. The privilege was waiting for me. Oh yes, I heard more than enough. And I was right, too. A voice. He was very little more than a voice. And I heard—him—it—this voice—other voices—all of them were so little more than voices—and the memory of that time itself lingers around me, impalpable, like a dying vibration of one immense jabber, silly, atrocious, sordid, savage, or simply mean, without any kind of sense. Voices, voices—even the girl herself—now—"

He was silent for a long time.

"I laid the ghost of his gifts at last with a lie," he began suddenly. "Girl! What? Did I mention a girl? Oh, she is out of it—completely. They—the women I mean—are out of it—should be out of it. We must help them to stay in that beautiful world of their own, lest ours gets worse. Oh, she had to be out of it. You should have heard the disinterred body of Mr. Kurtz saying, 'My Intended.' You would have perceived directly then how completely she was out of it. And the lofty frontal bone of Mr. Kurtz! They say the hair goes on growing sometimes, but this—ah—specimen was impressively bald. The wilderness had patted him on the head, and, behold, it was like a ball—an ivory ball; it had caressed him, and—lo!—he had withered; it had taken him, loved him, embraced him, got into his veins, consumed his flesh, and sealed his soul to its own by the inconceivable ceremonies of some devilish initiation. He was its spoiled and pampered favourite. Ivory? I should think so. Heaps of it, stacks of it. The old mud shanty was bursting with it. You would think there was not a single tusk left either above or below the ground in the whole country. 'Mostly fossil,' the manager had remarked disparagingly. It was no more fossil than I am; but they call it fossil when it is dug up. It appears these niggers do bury the tusks sometimes—but evidently they couldn't bury this parcel deep enough to save the gifted Mr. Kurtz from his fate. We filled the steamboat with it, and had to pile a lot on the deck. Thus he could see and enjoy as long as he could see, because the appreciation of this favour had remained with him to the last. You should have heard him say, 'My ivory.' Oh yes, I heard him. 'My Intended, my ivory, my station, my river, my—' everything belonged to him. It made me hold my breath in expectation of hearing the wilderness burst into a prodigious peal of laughter that would shake the fixed stars in their places. Everything belonged to him—but that was a trifle. The thing was to know what he belonged to, how many powers of darkness claimed him for their own. That was the reflection that made you creepy all over. It was impossible—it was not good for one either—trying to imagine. He had taken a high seat amongst the devils of the land—I mean literally. You can't understand. How could you?—with solid pavement under your feet, surrounded by kind neighbours ready to cheer you or to fall on you, stepping delicately between the butcher and the policeman, in the holy terror of scandal and gallows and lunatic asylums—how can you imagine what particular region of the first ages a man's untrammelled feet may take him into by the way of solitude—utter solitude without a policeman—by the way of silence—utter silence, where no warning voice of a kind neighbour can be heard whispering of public opinion? These little things make all the great difference. When they are gone you must fall back upon your own innate strength, upon your own capacity for faithfulness. Of course you may be too much of a fool to go wrong—too dull even to know you are being assaulted by the powers of darkness. I take it, no fool ever made a bargain for his soul with the devil: the fool is too much of a fool, or the devil too much of a devil—I don't know which. Or you may be such a thunderingly exalted creature as to be altogether deaf and blind to anything but heavenly sights and sounds. Then the earth for you is only a standing place—and whether to be like this is your loss or your gain I won't pretend to say. But most of us are neither one nor the other. The earth for us is a place to live in, where we must put up with sights, with sounds, with smells, too, by Jove!—breathe dead hippo, so to speak, and not be contaminated. And there, don't you see? your strength comes in, the faith in your ability for the digging of unostentatious holes to bury the stuff in—your power of devotion, not to yourself, but to an obscure, back-breaking business. And that's difficult enough. Mind, I am not trying to excuse or even explain—I am trying to account to myself for—for—Mr. Kurtz—for the shade of Mr. Kurtz. This initiated wraith from the back of Nowhere honoured me with its amazing confidence before it vanished altogether. This was because it could speak English to me. The original Kurtz had been educated partly in England, and—as he was good enough to say himself—his sympathies were in the right place. His mother was half-English, his father was half-French. All Europe contributed to the making of Kurtz; and by and by I learned that, most appropriately, the International Society for the Suppression of Savage Customs had entrusted him with the making of a report, for its future guidance. And he had written it too. I've seen it. I've read it. It was eloquent, vibrating with eloquence, but too high-strung, I think. Seventeen pages of close writing he had found time for! But this must have been before his—let us say—nerves went wrong, and caused him to preside at certain midnight dances ending with unspeakable rites, which—as far as I reluctantly gathered from what I heard at various times—were offered up to him—do you understand?—to Mr. Kurtz himself. But it was a beautiful piece of writing. The opening paragraph, however, in the light of later information, strikes me now as ominous. He began with the argument that we whites, from the point of development we had arrived at, 'must necessarily appear to them [savages] in the nature of supernatural beings—we approach them with the might as of a deity,' and so on, and so on. 'By the simple exercise of our will we can exert a power for good practically unbounded,' etc. etc. From that point he soared and took me with him. The peroration was magnificent, though difficult to remember, you know. It gave me the notion of an exotic Immensity ruled by an august Benevolence. It made me tingle with enthusiasm. This was the unbounded power of eloquence—of words—of burning noble words. There were no practical hints to interrupt the magic current of phrases, unless a kind of note at the foot of the last page, scrawled evidently much later, in an unsteady hand, may be regarded as the exposition of a method. It was very simple, and at the end of that moving appeal to every altruistic sentiment it blazed at you, luminous and terrifying, like a flash of lightning in a serene sky: 'Exterminate all the brutes!' The curious part was that he had apparently forgotten all about that valuable postscriptum, because, later on, when he in a sense came to himself, he repeatedly entreated me to take good care of 'my pamphlet' (he called it), as it was sure to have in the future a good influence upon his career. I had full information about all these things, and, besides, as it turned out, I was to have the care of his memory. I've done enough for it to give me the indisputable right to lay it, if I choose, for an everlasting rest in the dust-bin of progress, amongst all the sweepings and, figuratively speaking, all the dead cats of civilisation. But then, you see, I can't choose. He won't be forgotten. Whatever he was, he was not common. He had the power to charm or frighten rudimentary souls into an aggravated witch-dance in his honour; he could also fill the small souls of the pilgrims with bitter misgivings: he had one devoted friend at least, and he had conquered one soul in the world that was neither rudimentary nor tainted with self-seeking. No; I can't forget him, though I am not prepared to affirm the fellow was exactly worth the life we lost in getting to him. I missed my late helmsman awfully—I missed him even while his body was still lying in the pilot-house. Perhaps you will think it passing strange this regret for a savage who was no more account than a grain of sand in a black Sahara. Well, don't you see, he had done something, he had steered; for months I had him at my back—a help—an instrument. It was a kind of partnership. He steered for me—I had to look after him, I worried about his deficiencies, and thus a subtle bond had been created, of which I only became aware when it was suddenly broken. And the intimate profundity of that look he gave me when he received his hurt remains to this day in my memory—like a claim of distant kinship affirmed in a supreme moment.

"Poor fool! If he had only left that shutter alone. He had no restraint, no restraint—just like Kurtz—a tree swayed by the wind. As soon as I had put on a dry pair of slippers, I dragged him out, after first jerking the spear out of his side, which operation I confess I performed with my eyes shut tight. His heels leaped together over the little doorstep; his shoulders were pressed to my breast; I hugged him from behind desperately. Oh! he was heavy, heavy; heavier than any man on earth, I should imagine. Then without more ado I tipped him overboard. The current snatched him as though he had been a wisp of grass, and I saw the body roll over twice before I lost sight of it for ever. All the pilgrims and the manager were then congregated on the awning-deck about the pilot-house, chattering at each other like a flock of excited magpies, and there was a scandalised murmur at my heartless promptitude. What they wanted to keep that body hanging about for I can't guess. Embalm it, maybe. But I had also heard another, and a very ominous, murmur on the deck below. My friends the wood-cutters were likewise scandalised, and with a better show of reason—though I admit that the reason itself was quite inadmissible. Oh, quite! I had made up my mind that if my late helmsman was to be eaten, the fishes alone should have him. He had been a very second-rate helmsman while alive, but now he was dead he might have become a first-class temptation, and possibly cause some startling trouble. Besides, I was anxious to take the wheel, the man in pink pyjamas showing himself a hopeless duffer at the business.

"This I did directly the simple funeral was over. We were going half-speed, keeping right in the middle of the stream, and I listened to the talk about me. They had given up Kurtz, they had given up the station; Kurtz was dead, and the station had been burnt—and so on—and so on. The red-haired pilgrim was beside himself with the thought that at least this poor Kurtz had been properly revenged. 'Say! We must have made a glorious slaughter of them in the bush. Eh? What do you think? Say?' He positively danced, the bloodthirsty little gingery beggar. And he had nearly fainted when he saw the wounded man! I could not help saying, 'You made a glorious lot of smoke, anyhow.' I had seen, from the way the tops of the bushes rustled and flew, that almost all the shots had gone too high. You can't hit anything unless you take aim and fire from the shoulder; but these chaps fired from the hip with their eyes shut. The retreat, I maintained—and I was right—was caused by the screeching of the steam-whistle. Upon this they forgot Kurtz, and began to howl at me with indignant protests.

"The manager stood by the wheel murmuring confidentially about the necessity of getting well away down the river before dark at all events, when I saw in the distance a clearing on the river-side and the outlines of some sort of building. 'What's this?' I asked. He clapped his hands in wonder. 'The station!' he cried. I edged in at once, still going half-speed.

"Through my glasses I saw the slope of a hill interspersed with rare trees and perfectly free from undergrowth. A long decaying building on the summit was half buried in the high grass; the large holes in the peaked roof gaped black from afar; the jungle and the woods made a background. There was no enclosure or fence of any kind; but there had been one apparently, for near the house half a dozen slim posts remained in a row, roughly trimmed, and with their upper ends ornamented with round carved balls. The rails, or whatever there had been between, had disappeared. Of course the forest surrounded all that. The river-bank was clear, and on the water side I saw a white man under a hat like a cart-wheel beckoning persistently with his whole arm. Examining the edge of the forest above and below, I was almost certain I could see movements—human forms gliding here and there. I steamed past prudently, then stopped the engines and let her drift down. The man on the shore began to shout, urging us to land. 'We have been attacked,' screamed the manager. 'I know—I know. It's all right,' yelled back the other, as cheerful as you please. 'Come along. It's all right. I am glad.'

"His aspect reminded me of something I had seen—something funny I had seen somewhere. As I manœuvred to get alongside, I was asking myself, 'What does this fellow look like?' Suddenly I got it. He looked like a harlequin. His clothes had been made of some stuff that was brown holland probably, but it was covered with patches all over, with bright patches, blue, red, and yellow—patches on the back, patches on the front, patches on elbows, on knees; coloured binding round his jacket, scarlet edging at the bottom of his trousers; and the sunshine made him look extremely gay and wonderfully neat withal, because you could see how beautifully all this patching had been done. A beardless, boyish face, very fair, no features to speak of, nose peeling, little blue eyes, smiles and frowns chasing each other over that open countenance like sunshine and shadow on a wind-swept plain. 'Look out, captain!' he cried; 'there's a snag lodged in here last night.' What! Another snag? I confess I swore shamefully. I had nearly holed my cripple, to finish off that charming trip. The harlequin on the bank turned his little pug nose up to me. 'You English?' he asked, all smiles. 'Are you?' I shouted from the wheel. The smiles vanished, and he shook his head as if sorry for my disappointment. Then he brightened up. 'Never mind!' he cried encouragingly. 'Are we in time?' I asked. 'He is up there,' he replied, with a toss of the head up the hill, and becoming gloomy all of a sudden. His face was like the autumn sky, overcast one moment and bright the next.

"When the manager, escorted by the pilgrims, all of them armed to the teeth, had gone to the house, this chap came on board. 'I say, I don't like this. These natives are in the bush,' I said. He assured me earnestly it was all right. 'They are simple people,' he added; 'well, I am glad you came. It took me all my time to keep them off.' 'But you said it was all right,' I cried. 'Oh, they meant no harm,' he said; and as I stared he corrected himself, 'Not exactly.' Then vivaciously, 'My faith, your pilot-house wants a clean up!' In the next breath he advised me to keep enough steam on the boiler to blow the whistle in case of any trouble. 'One good screech will do more for you than all your rifles. They are simple people,' he repeated. He rattled away at such a rate he quite overwhelmed me. He seemed to be trying to make up for lots of silence, and actually hinted, laughing, that such was the case. 'Don't you talk with Mr. Kurtz?' I said. 'You don't talk with that man—you listen to him,' he exclaimed with severe exaltation. 'But now—' He waved his arm, and in the twinkling of an eye was in the uttermost depths of despondency. In a moment he came up again with a jump, possessed himself of both my hands, shook them continuously, while he gabbled: 'Brother sailor ... honour ... pleasure ... delight ... introduce myself ... Russian ... son of an arch-priest ... Government of Tambov ... What? Tobacco! English tobacco; the excellent English tobacco! Now, that's brotherly. Smoke? Where's a sailor that does not smoke?'

"The pipe soothed him, and gradually I made out he had run away from school, had gone to sea in a Russian ship; ran away again; served some time in English ships; was now reconciled with the arch-priest. He made a point of that. 'But when one is young one must see things, gather experience, ideas; enlarge the mind.' 'Here!' I interrupted. 'You can never tell! Here I met Mr. Kurtz,' he said, youthfully solemn and reproachful. I held my tongue after that. It appears he had persuaded a Dutch trading-house on the coast to fit him out with stores and goods, and had started for the interior with a light heart, and no more idea of what would happen to him than a baby. He had been wandering about that river for nearly two years alone, cut off from everybody and everything. 'I am not so young as I look. I am twenty-five,' he said. 'At first old Van Shuyten would tell me to go to the devil,' he narrated with keen enjoyment; 'but I stuck to him, and talked and talked, till at last he got afraid I would talk the hind-leg off his favourite dog, so he gave me some cheap things and a few guns, and told me he hoped he would never see my face again. Good old Dutchman, Van Shuyten. I sent him one small lot of ivory a year ago, so that he can't call me a little thief when I get back. I hope he got it. And for the rest I don't care. I had some wood stacked for you. That was my old house. Did you see?'

"I gave him Towson's book. He made as though he would kiss me, but restrained himself. 'The only book I had left, and I thought I had lost it,' he said, looking at it ecstatically. 'So many accidents happen to a man going about alone, you know. Canoes get upset sometimes—and sometimes you've got to clear out so quick when the people get angry.' He thumbed the pages. 'You made notes in Russian?' I asked. He nodded. 'I thought they were written in cipher,' I said. He laughed, then became serious. 'I had lots of trouble to keep these people off,' he said. 'Did they want to kill you?' I asked. 'Oh no!' he cried, and checked himself. 'Why did they attack us?' I pursued. He hesitated, then said shamefacedly, 'They don't want him to go.' 'Don't they?' I said curiously. He nodded a nod full of mystery and wisdom. 'I tell you,' he cried, 'this man has enlarged my mind.' He opened his arms wide, staring at me with his little blue eyes that were perfectly round."

III

"I looked at him, lost in astonishment. There he was before me, in motley, as though he had absconded from a troupe of mimes, enthusiastic, fabulous. His very existence was improbable, inexplicable, and altogether bewildering. He was an insoluble problem. It was inconceivable how he had existed, how he had succeeded in getting so far, how he had managed to remain—why he did not instantly disappear. 'I went a little farther,' he said, 'then still a little farther—till I had gone so far that I don't know how I'll ever get back. Never mind. Plenty time. I can manage. You take Kurtz away quick—quick—I tell you.' The glamour of youth enveloped his particoloured rags, his destitution, his loneliness, the essential desolation of his futile wanderings. For months—for years—his life hadn't been worth a day's purchase; and there he was gallantly, thoughtlessly alive, to all appearance indestructible solely by the virtue of his few years and of his unreflecting audacity. I was seduced into something like admiration—like envy. Glamour urged him on, glamour kept him unscathed. He surely wanted nothing from the wilderness but space to breathe in and to push on through. His need was to exist, and to move onwards at the greatest possible risk, and with a maximum of privation. If the absolutely pure, uncalculating, unpractical spirit of adventure had ever ruled a human being, it ruled this be-patched youth. I almost envied him the possession of this modest and clear flame. It seemed to have consumed all thought of self so completely, that, even while he was talking to you, you forgot that it was he—the man before your eyes—who had gone through these things. I did not envy him his devotion to Kurtz, though. He had not meditated over it. It came to him, and he accepted it with a sort of eager fatalism. I must say that to me it appeared about the most dangerous thing in every way he had come upon so far.

"They had come together unavoidably, like two ships becalmed near each other, and lay rubbing sides at last. I suppose Kurtz wanted an audience, because on a certain occasion, when encamped in the forest, they had talked all night, or more probably Kurtz had talked. 'We talked of everything,' he said, quite transported at the recollection. 'I forgot there was such a thing as sleep. The night did not seem to last an hour. Everything! Everything! . . . Of love too.' 'Ah, he talked to you of love!' I said, much amused. 'It isn't what you think,' he cried, almost passionately. 'It was in general. He made me see things—things.'

"He threw his arms up. We were on deck at the time, and the head-man of my wood-cutters, lounging near by, turned upon him his heavy and glittering eyes. I looked around, and I don't know why, but I assure you that never, never before, did this land, this river, this jungle, the very arch of this blazing sky, appear to me so hopeless and so dark, so impenetrable to human thought, so pitiless to human weakness. 'And, ever since, you have been with him, of course?' I said.

"On the contrary. It appears their intercourse had been very much broken by various causes. He had, as he informed me proudly, managed to nurse Kurtz through two illnesses (he alluded to it as you would to some risky feat), but as a rule Kurtz wandered alone, far in the depths of the forest. 'Very often coming to this station, I had to wait days and days before he would turn up,' he said. 'Ah, it was worth waiting for!—sometimes.' 'What was he doing? exploring or what?' I asked. 'Oh yes, of course'; he had discovered lots of villages, a lake too—he did not know exactly in what direction; it was dangerous to inquire too much—but mostly his expeditions had been for ivory. 'But he had no goods to trade with by that time,' I objected. 'There's a good lot of cartridges left even yet,' he answered, looking away. 'To speak plainly, he raided the country,' I said. He nodded. 'Not alone, surely!' He muttered something about the villages round that lake. 'Kurtz got the tribe to follow him, did he?' I suggested. He fidgeted a little. 'They adored him,' he said. The tone of these words was so extraordinary that I looked at him searchingly. It was curious to see his mingled eagerness and reluctance to speak of Kurtz. The man filled his life, occupied his thoughts, swayed his emotions. 'What can you expect?' he burst out; 'he came to them with thunder and lightning, you know—and they had never seen anything like it—and very terrible. He could be very terrible. You can't judge Mr. Kurtz as you would an ordinary man. No, no, no! Now—just to give you an idea—I don't mind telling you, he wanted to shoot me too one day—but I don't judge him.' 'Shoot you!' I cried. 'What for?' 'Well, I had a small lot of ivory the chief of that village near my house gave me. You see I used to shoot game for them. Well, he wanted it, and wouldn't hear reason. He declared he would shoot me unless I gave him the ivory and then cleared out of the country, because he could do so, and had a fancy for it, and there was nothing on earth to prevent him killing whom he jolly well pleased. And it was true too. I gave him the ivory. What did I care! But I didn't clear out. No, no. I couldn't leave him. I had to be careful, of course, till we got friendly again for a time. He had his second illness then. Afterwards I had to keep out of the way; but I didn't mind. He was living for the most part in those villages on the lake. When he came down to the river, sometimes he would take to me, and sometimes it was better for me to be careful. This man suffered too much. He hated all this, and somehow he couldn't get away. When I had a chance I begged him to try and leave while there was time; I offered to go back with him. And he would say yes, and then he would remain; go off on another ivory hunt; disappear for weeks; forget himself amongst these people—forget himself—you know.' 'Why! he's mad,' I said. He protested indignantly. Mr. Kurtz couldn't be mad. If I had heard him talk, only two days ago, I wouldn't dare hint at such a thing.... I had taken up my binoculars while we talked, and was looking at the shore, sweeping the limit of the forest at each side and at the back of the house. The consciousness of there being people in that bush, so silent, so quiet—as silent and quiet as the ruined house on the hill—made me uneasy. There was no sign on the face of nature of this amazing tale that was not so much told as suggested to me in desolate exclamations, completed by shrugs, in interrupted phrases, in hints ending in deep sighs. The woods were unmoved, like a mask—heavy, like the closed door of a prison—they looked with their air of hidden knowledge, of patient expectation, of unapproachable silence. The Russian was explaining to me that it was only lately that Mr. Kurtz had come down to the river, bringing along with him all the fighting men of that lake tribe. He had been absent for several months—getting himself adored, I suppose—and had come down unexpectedly, with the intention to all appearance of making a raid either across the river or down stream. Evidently the appetite for more ivory had got the better of the—what shall I say?—less material aspirations. However, he had got much worse suddenly. 'I heard he was lying helpless, and so I came up—took my chance,' said the Russian. 'Oh, he is bad, very bad.' I directed my glass to the house. There were no signs of life, but there was the ruined roof, the long mud wall peeping above the grass, with three little square window-holes, no two of the same size; all this brought within reach of my hand, as it were. And then I made a brusque movement, and one of the remaining posts of that vanished fence leaped up in the field of my glass. You remember I told you I had been struck at the distance by certain attempts at ornamentation, rather remarkable in the ruinous aspect of the place. Now I had suddenly a nearer view, and its first result was to make me throw my head back as if before a blow. Then I went carefully from post to post with my glass, and I saw my mistake. These round knobs were not ornamental but symbolic; they were expressive and puzzling, striking and disturbing—food for thought and also for the vultures if there had been any looking down from the sky; but at all events for such ants as were industrious enough to ascend the pole. They would have been even more impressive, those heads on the stakes, if their faces had not been turned to the house. Only one, the first I had made out, was facing my way. I was not so shocked as you may think. The start back I had given was really nothing but a movement of surprise. I had expected to see a knob of wood there, you know. I returned deliberately to the first I had seen—and there it was, black, dried, sunken, with closed eyelids—a head that seemed to sleep at the top of that pole, and, with the shrunken dry lips showing a narrow white line of the teeth, was smiling too, smiling continuously at some endless and jocose dream of that eternal slumber.

"I am not disclosing any trade secrets. In fact the manager said afterwards that Mr. Kurtz's methods had ruined the district. I have no opinion on that point, but I want you clearly to understand that there was nothing exactly profitable in these heads being there. They only showed that Mr. Kurtz lacked restraint in the gratification of his various lusts, that there was something wanting in him—some small matter which, when the pressing need arose, could not be found under his magnificent eloquence. Whether he knew of this deficiency himself I can't say. I think the knowledge came to him at last—only at the very last. But the wilderness had found him out early, and had taken on him a terrible vengeance for the fantastic invasion. I think it had whispered to him things about himself which he did not know, things of which he had no conception till he took counsel with this great solitude—and the whisper had proved irresistibly fascinating. It echoed loudly within him because he was hollow at the core. . . . I put down the glass, and the head that had appeared near enough to be spoken to seemed at once to have leaped away from me into inaccessible distance.

"The admirer of Mr. Kurtz was a bit crestfallen. In a hurried, indistinct voice he began to assure me he had not dared to take these—say, symbols—down. He was not afraid of the natives; they would not stir till Mr. Kurtz gave the word. His ascendancy was extraordinary. The camps of these people surrounded the place, and the chiefs came every day to see him. They would crawl . . . 'I don't want to know anything of the ceremonies used when approaching Mr. Kurtz,' I shouted. Curious, this feeling that came over me that such details would be more intolerable than those heads drying on the stakes under Mr.

Kurtz's windows. After all, that was only a savage sight, while I seemed at one bound to have been transported into some lightless region of subtle horrors, where pure, uncomplicated savagery was a positive relief, being something that had a right to exist—obviously—in the sunshine. The young man looked at me with surprise. I suppose it did not occur to him that Mr. Kurtz was no idol of mine. He forgot I hadn't heard any of these splendid monologues on, what was it? on love, justice, conduct of life—or what not. If it had come to crawling before Mr. Kurtz, he crawled as much as the veriest savage of them all. I had no idea of the conditions, he said: these heads were the heads of rebels. I shocked him excessively by laughing. Rebels! What would be the next definition I was to hear? There had been enemies, criminals, workers—and these were rebels. Those rebellious heads looked very subdued to me on their sticks. 'You don't know how such a life tries a man like Kurtz,' cried Kurtz's last disciple. 'Well, and you?' I said. 'I! I! I am a simple man. I have no great thoughts. I want nothing from anybody. How can you compare me to . . . ?' His feelings were too much for speech, and suddenly he broke down. 'I don't understand,' he groaned. 'I've been doing my best to keep him alive, and that's enough. I had no hand in all this. I have no abilities. There hasn't been a drop of medicine or a mouthful of invalid food for months here. He was shamefully abandoned. A man like this, with such ideas. Shamefully! Shamefully! I—I—haven't slept for the last ten nights. . . .'

"His voice lost itself in the calm of the evening. The long shadows of the forest had slipped down hill while we talked, had gone far beyond the ruined hovel, beyond the symbolic row of stakes. All this was in the gloom, while we down there were yet in the sunshine, and the stretch of the river abreast of the clearing glittered in a still and dazzling splendour, with a murky and overshadowed bend above and below. Not a living soul was seen on the shore. The bushes did not rustle.

"Suddenly round the corner of the house a group of men appeared, as though they had come up from the ground. They waded waist-deep in the grass, in a compact body, bearing an improvised stretcher in their midst. Instantly, in the emptiness of the landscape, a cry arose whose shrillness pierced the still air like a sharp arrow flying straight to the very heart of the land; and, as if by enchantment, streams of human beings—of naked human beings—with spears in their hands, with bows, with shields, with wild glances and savage movements, were poured into the clearing by the dark-faced and pensive forest. The bushes shook, the grass swayed for a time, and then everything stood still in attentive immobility.

" 'Now, if he does not say the right thing to them we are all done for,' said the Russian at my elbow. The knot of men with the stretcher had stopped too, half-way to the steamer, as if petrified. I saw the man on the stretcher sit up, lank and with an uplifted arm, above the shoulders of the bearers. 'Let us hope that the man who can talk so well of love in general will find some particular reason to spare us this time,' I said. I resented bitterly the absurd danger of our situation, as if to be at the mercy of that atrocious phantom had been a dishonouring necessity. I could not hear a sound, but through my glasses I saw the thin arm extended commandingly, the lower jaw moving, the eyes of that apparition shining darkly far in its bony head that nodded with grotesque jerks. Kurtz—Kurtz—that means 'short' in German—don't it? Well, the name was as true as everything else in his life—and death. He looked at least seven feet long. His covering had fallen off, and his body emerged from it pitiful and appalling as from a winding-sheet. I could see the cage of his ribs all astir, the bones of his arm waving. It was as though an animated image of death carved out of old ivory had been shaking its hand with menaces at a motionless crowd of men made of dark and glittering bronze. I saw him open his mouth wide—it gave him a weirdly voracious aspect, as though he had wanted to swallow all the air, all the earth, all the men before him. A deep voice reached me faintly. He must have been shouting. He fell back suddenly. The stretcher shook as the bearers staggered forward again, and almost at the same time I noticed that the crowd of savages was vanishing without any perceptible movement of retreat, as if the forest that had ejected these beings so suddenly had drawn them in again as the breath is drawn in a long aspiration.

"Some of the pilgrims behind the stretcher carried his arms—two shot-guns, a heavy rifle, and a light revolver-carbine—the thunderbolts of that pitiful Jupiter. The manager bent over him murmuring as he walked beside his head. They laid him down in one of the little cabins—just a room for a bedplace and a camp-stool or two, you know. We had brought his belated correspondence, and a lot of torn envelopes and open letters littered his bed. His hand roamed feebly amongst these papers. I was struck by the fire of his eyes and the composed languor of his expression. It was not so much the exhaustion of disease. He did not seem in pain. This shadow looked satiated and calm, as though for the moment it had had its fill of all the emotions.

"He rustled one of the letters, and looking straight in my face said, 'I am glad.' Somebody had been writing to him about me. These special recommendations were turning up again. The volume of tone he emitted without effort, almost without the trouble of moving his lips, amazed me. A voice! a voice! It was grave, profound, vibrating, while the man did not seem capable of a whisper. However, he had enough strength in him—factitious no doubt—to very nearly make an end of us, as you shall hear directly.

"The manager appeared silently in the doorway; I stepped out at once and he drew the curtain after me. The Russian, eyed curiously by the pilgrims, was staring at the shore. I followed the direction of his glance.

"Dark human shapes could be made out in the distance, flitting indistinctly against the gloomy border of the forest, and near the river two bronze figures, leaning on tall spears, stood in the sunlight under fantastic head-dresses of spotted skins, warlike and still in statuesque repose. And from right to left along the lighted shore moved a wild and gorgeous apparition of a woman.

"She walked with measured steps, draped in striped and fringed cloths, treading the earth proudly, with a slight jingle and flash of barbarous ornaments. She carried her head high; her hair was done in the shape of a helmet; she had brass leggings to the knee, brass wire gauntlets to the elbow, a crimson spot on her tawny cheek, innumerable necklaces of glass beads on her neck; bizarre things, charms, gifts of witch-men, that hung about her, glittered and trembled at every step. She must have had the value of several elephant tusks upon her. She was savage and superb, wild-eyed and magnificent; there was something ominous and stately in her deliberate progress. And in the hush that had fallen suddenly upon the whole sorrowful land, the immense wilderness, the colossal body of the fecund and mysterious life seemed to look at her, pensive, as though it had been looking at the image of its own tenebrous and passionate soul.

"She came abreast of the steamer, stood still, and faced us. Her long shadow fell to the water's edge. Her face had a tragic and fierce aspect of wild sorrow and of dumb pain mingled with the fear of some struggling, half-shaped resolve. She stood looking at us without a stir, and like the wilderness itself, with an air of brooding over an inscrutable purpose. A whole minute passed, and then she made a step forward. There was a low jingle, a glint of yellow metal, a sway of fringed draperies, and she stopped as if her heart had failed her. The young fellow by my side growled. The pilgrims murmured at my back. She looked at us all as if her life had depended upon the unswerving steadiness of her glance. Suddenly she opened her bared arms and threw them up rigid above her head, as though in an uncontrollable desire to touch the sky, and at the same time the swift shadows darted out on the earth, swept around on the river, gathering the steamer into a shadowy embrace. A formidable silence hung over the scene.

"She turned away slowly, walked on, following the bank, and passed into the bushes to the left. Once only her eyes gleamed back at us in the dusk of the thickets before she disappeared.

" 'If she had offered to come aboard I really think I would have tried to shoot her,' said the man of patches nervously. 'I had been risking my life every day for the last fortnight to keep her out of the house. She got in one day and kicked up a row about those miserable rags I picked up in the storeroom to mend my clothes with. I wasn't decent. At least it must have been that, for she talked like a fury to Kurtz for an hour, pointing at me now and then. I don't understand the dialect of this tribe. Luckily for me, I fancy Kurtz felt too ill that day to care, or there would have been mischief. I don't understand.... No—it's too much for me. Ah, well, it's all over now.'

"At this moment I heard Kurtz's deep voice behind the curtain: 'Save me!—save the ivory, you mean. Don't tell me. Save *me*! Why, I've had to save you. You are interrupting my plans now. Sick! Sick! Not so sick as you would like to believe. Never mind. I'll carry my ideas out yet—I will return. I'll show you what can be done. You with your little peddling notions—you are interfering with me. I will return. I ...'

"The manager came out. He did me the honour to take me under the arm and lead me aside. 'He is very low, very low,' he said. He considered it necessary to sigh, but neglected to be consistently sorrowful. 'We have done all we could for him—haven't we? But there is no disguising the fact, Mr. Kurtz has done more harm than good to the Company. He did not see the time was not ripe for vigorous action. Cautiously, cautiously—that's my principle. We must be cautious yet. The district is closed to us for a time. Deplorable! Upon the whole, the trade will suffer. I don't deny there is a remarkable quantity of ivory—mostly fossil. We must save it, at all events—but look how precarious the position is—and why? Because the method is unsound.' 'Do you,' said I, looking at the shore, 'call it "unsound method"?' 'Without doubt,' he exclaimed hotly. 'Don't you?' ... 'No method at all,' I murmured after a while. 'Exactly,' he exulted. 'I anticipated this. Shows a complete want of judgment. It is my duty to point it out in the proper quarter.' 'Oh,' said I, 'that fellow—what's his name?—the brickmaker, will make a readable report for you.' He appeared confounded for a moment. It seemed to me I had never breathed an atmosphere so vile, and I turned mentally to Kurtz for relief—positively for relief. 'Nevertheless, I think Mr. Kurtz is a remarkable man,' I said with emphasis. He started, dropped on me a cold heavy glance, said very quietly, 'He *was*,' and turned his back on me. My hour of favour was over; I found myself lumped along with Kurtz as a partisan of methods for which the time was not ripe: I was unsound! Ah! but it was something to have at least a choice of nightmares.

"I had turned to the wilderness really, not to Mr. Kurtz, who, I was ready to admit, was as good as buried. And for a moment it seemed to me as if I also were buried in a vast grave full of unspeakable secrets. I felt an intolerable weight oppressing my breast, the smell of the damp earth, the unseen presence of victorious corruption, the darkness of an impenetrable night.... The Russian tapped me on the shoulder. I heard him mumbling and stammering something about 'brother seaman—couldn't conceal—knowledge of matters that would affect Mr. Kurtz's reputation.' I waited. For him evidently Mr. Kurtz was not in his grave; I suspect that for him Mr. Kurtz was one of the immortals. 'Well!' said I at last, 'speak out. As it happens, I am Mr. Kurtz's friend—in a way.'

"He stated with a good deal of formality that had we not been 'of the same profession,' he would have kept the matter to himself without regard to consequences. He suspected 'there was an active ill-will towards him on the part of these white men that—' 'You are right,' I said, remembering a certain conversation I had overheard. 'The manager thinks you ought to be hanged.' He showed a concern at this intelligence which amused me at first. 'I had better get out of the way quietly,' he said earnestly. 'I can do no more for Kurtz now, and they would soon find some excuse. What's to stop them? There's a military post three hundred miles from here.' 'Well, upon my word,' said I, 'perhaps you had better go if you have any friends amongst the savages near by.' 'Plenty,' he said. 'They are simple people—and I want nothing, you know.' He stood biting his lip, then: 'I don't want any harm to happen to these whites here, but of course I was thinking of Mr. Kurtz's reputation—but you are a brother seaman and—' 'All right,' said I, after a time. 'Mr. Kurtz's reputation is safe with me.' I did not know how truly I spoke.

"He informed me, lowering his voice, that it was Kurtz who had ordered the attack to be made on the steamer. 'He hated sometimes the idea of being taken away—and then again . . . But I don't understand these matters. I am a simple man. He thought it would scare you away—that you would give it up, thinking him dead. I could not stop him. Oh, I had an awful time of it this last month.' 'Very well,' I said. 'He is all right now.' 'Ye-e-es,' he muttered, not very convinced apparently. 'Thanks,' said I; 'I shall keep my eyes open.' 'But quiet—eh?' he urged anxiously. 'It would be awful for his reputation if anybody here—' I promised a complete discretion with great gravity. 'I have a canoe and three black fellows waiting not very far. I am off. Could you give me a few Martini-Henry cartridges?' I could, and did, with proper secrecy. He helped himself, with a wink at me, to a handful of my tobacco. 'Between sailors—you know—good English tobacco.' At the door of the pilot-house he turned round—'I say, haven't you a pair of shoes you could spare?' He raised one leg. 'Look.' The soles were tied with knotted strings sandal-wise under his bare feet. I rooted out an old pair, at which he looked with admiration before tucking it under his left arm. One of his pockets (bright red) was bulging with cartridges, from the other (dark blue) peeped 'Towson's Inquiry,' etc. etc. He seemed to think himself excellently well equipped for a renewed encounter with the wilderness. 'Ah! I'll never, never meet such a man again. You ought to have heard him recite poetry—his own too it was, he told me. Poetry!' He rolled his eyes at the recollection of these delights. 'Oh, he enlarged my mind!' 'Good-bye,' said I. He shook hands and vanished in the night. Sometimes I ask myself whether I had ever really seen him—whether it was possible to meet such a phenomenon! . . .

"When I woke up shortly after midnight his warning came to my mind with its hint of danger that seemed, in the starred darkness, real enough to make me get up for the purpose of having a look round. On the hill a big fire burned, illuminating fitfully a crooked corner of the station-house. One of the agents with a picket of a few of our blacks, armed for the purpose, was keeping guard over the ivory; but deep within the forest, red gleams that wavered, that seemed to sink and rise from the ground amongst confused columnar shapes of intense blackness, showed the exact position of the camp where Mr. Kurtz's adorers were keeping their uneasy vigil. The monotonous beating of a big drum filled the air with muffled shocks and a lingering vibration. A steady droning sound of many men chanting each to himself some weird incantation came out from the black, flat wall of the woods as the humming of bees comes out of a hive, and had a strange narcotic effect upon my half-awake senses. I believe I dozed off leaning over the rail, till an abrupt burst of yells, an overwhelming outbreak of a pent-up and mysterious frenzy, woke me up in a bewildered wonder. It was cut short all at once, and the low droning went on with an effect of audible and soothing silence. I glanced casually into the little cabin. A light was burning within, but Mr. Kurtz was not there.

"I think I would have raised an outcry if I had believed my eyes. But I didn't believe them at first—the thing seemed so impossible. The fact is I was completely unnerved by a sheer blank fright, pure abstract terror, unconnected with any distinct shape of physical danger. What made this emotion so overpowering was—how shall I define it?—the moral shock I received, as if something altogether monstrous, intolerable to thought and odious to the soul, had been thrust upon me unexpectedly. This lasted of course the merest fraction of a second, and then the usual sense of commonplace, deadly danger, the possibility of a sudden onslaught and massacre, or something of the kind, which I saw impending, was positively welcome and composing. It pacified me, in fact, so much, that I did not raise an alarm.

"There was an agent buttoned up inside an ulster and sleeping on a chair on deck within three feet of me. The yells had not awakened him; he snored very slightly; I left him to his slumbers and leaped ashore. I did not betray Mr. Kurtz—it was ordered I should never betray him—it was written I should be loyal to the nightmare of my choice. I was anxious to deal with this shadow by myself alone—and to this day I don't know why I was so jealous of sharing with any one the peculiar blackness of that experience.

"As soon as I got on the bank I saw a trail—a broad trail through the grass. I remember the exultation with which I said to myself, 'He can't walk—he is crawling on all-fours—I've got him.' The grass was wet with dew. I strode rapidly with clenched fists. I fancy I had some vague notion of falling upon him and giving him a drubbing. I don't know. I had some imbecile thoughts. The knitting old woman with the cat obtruded herself upon my memory as a most improper person to be sitting at the other end of such an affair. I saw a row of pilgrims squirting lead in the air out of Winchesters held to the hip. I thought I would never get back to the steamer, and imagined myself living alone and unarmed in the woods to an advanced age. Such silly things—you know. And I remember I confounded the beat of the drum with the beating of my heart, and was pleased at its calm regularity.

"I kept to the track though—then stopped to listen. The night was very clear; a dark blue space, sparkling with dew and starlight, in which black things stood very still. I thought I could see a kind of motion ahead of me. I was strangely cocksure of everything that night. I actually left the track and ran in a wide semicircle (I verily believe chuckling to myself) so as to get in front of that stir, of that motion I had seen—if indeed I had seen anything. I was circumventing Kurtz as though it had been a boyish game.

"I came upon him, and, if he had not heard me coming, I would have fallen over him too, but he got up in time. He rose, unsteady, long, pale, indistinct, like a vapour exhaled by the earth, and swayed slightly, misty and silent before me; while at my back the fires loomed between the trees, and the murmur of many voices issued from the forest. I had cut him off cleverly; but when actually confronting him I seemed to come to my senses, I saw the danger in its right proportion. It was by no means over yet. Suppose he began to shout? Though he could hardly stand, there was still plenty of vigour in his voice. 'Go away—hide yourself,' he said, in that profound tone. It was very awful. I glanced back. We were within thirty yards of the nearest fire. A black figure stood up, strode on long black legs, waving long black arms, across the glow. It had horns—antelope horns, I think—on its head. Some sorcerer, some witch-man no doubt: it looked fiend-like enough. 'Do you know what you are doing?' I whispered. 'Perfectly,' he answered, raising his voice for that single word: it sounded to me far off and yet loud, like a hail through a speaking-trumpet. If he makes a row we are lost, I thought to myself. This clearly was not a case for fisticuffs, even apart from the very natural aversion I had to beat that Shadow—this wandering and tormented thing. 'You will be lost,' I said—'utterly lost.' One gets sometimes such a flash of inspiration, you know. I did say the right thing, though indeed he could not have been more irretrievably lost than he was at this very moment, when the foundations of our intimacy were being laid—to endure—to endure—even to the end—even beyond.

" 'I had immense plans,' he muttered irresolutely. 'Yes,' said I; 'but if you try to shout I'll smash your head with—' There was not a stick or a stone near. 'I will throttle you for good,' I corrected myself. 'I was on the threshold of great things,' he pleaded, in a voice of longing, with a wistfulness of tone that made my blood run cold. 'And now for this stupid scoundrel—' 'Your success in Europe is assured in any case,' I affirmed steadily. I did not want to have the throttling of him, you understand—and indeed it would have been very little use for any practical purpose. I tried to break the spell—the heavy, mute spell of the wilderness—that seemed to draw him to its pitiless breast by the awakening of forgotten and brutal instincts, by the memory of gratified and monstrous passions. This alone, I was convinced, had driven him out to the edge of the forest, to the bush, towards the gleam of fires, the throb of drums, the drone of weird incantations; this alone had beguiled his unlawful soul beyond the bounds of permitted aspirations. And, don't you see, the terror of the position was not in being knocked on the head—though I had a very lively sense of that danger too—but in this, that I had to deal with a being to whom I could not appeal in the name of anything high or low. I had, even like the niggers, to invoke him—himself—his own exalted and incredible degradation. There was nothing either above or below him, and I knew it. He had kicked himself loose of the earth. Confound the man! he had kicked the very earth to pieces. He was alone, and I before him did not know whether I stood on the ground or floated in the air. I've been telling you what we said—repeating the phrases we pronounced—but what's the good? They were common everyday words—the familiar, vague sounds exchanged on every waking day of life. But what of that? They had behind them, to my mind, the terrific suggestiveness of words heard in dreams, of phrases spoken in nightmares. Soul! If anybody had ever struggled with a soul, I am the man. And I wasn't arguing with a lunatic either. Believe me or not, his intelligence was perfectly clear—concentrated, it is true, upon himself with horrible intensity, yet clear; and therein was my only chance—barring, of course, the killing him there and then, which wasn't so good, on account of unavoidable noise. But his soul was mad. Being alone in the wilderness, it had looked within itself, and, by heavens! I tell you, it had gone mad. I had—for my sins, I suppose, to go through the ordeal of looking into it myself. No eloquence could have been so withering to one's belief in mankind as his final burst of sincerity. He struggled with himself too. I saw it—I heard it. I saw the inconceivable mystery of a soul that knew no restraint, no faith, and no fear, yet struggling blindly with itself. I kept my head pretty well; but when I had him at last stretched on the couch, I wiped my forehead, while my legs shook under me as though I had carried half a ton on my back down that hill. And yet I had only supported him, his bony arm clasped round my neck—and he was not much heavier than a child.

"When next day we left at noon, the crowd, of whose presence behind the curtain of trees I had been acutely conscious all the time, flowed out of the woods again, filled the clearing, covered the slope with a mass of naked, breathing, quivering, bronze bodies. I steamed up a bit, then swung down-stream, and two thousand eyes followed the evolutions of the splashing, thumping, fierce river-demon beating the water with its terrible tail and breathing black smoke into the air. In front of the first rank, along the river, three men, plastered with bright red earth from head to foot, strutted to and fro restlessly. When we came abreast again, they faced the river, stamped their feet, nodded their horned heads, swayed their scarlet bodies; they shook towards the fierce river-demon a bunch of black feathers, a mangy skin with a pendent tail—something that looked like a dried gourd; they shouted periodically together strings of amazing words that resembled no sounds of human language; and the deep murmurs of the crowd, interrupted suddenly, were like the responses of some satanic litany.

"We had carried Kurtz into the pilot-house: there was more air there. Lying on the couch, he stared through the open shutter. There was an eddy in the mass of human bodies, and the woman with helmeted head and tawny cheeks rushed out to the very brink of the stream. She put out her hands, shouted something, and all that wild mob took up the shout in a roaring chorus of articulated, rapid, breathless utterance.

" 'Do you understand this?' I asked.

"He kept on looking out past me with fiery, longing eyes, with a mingled expression of wistfulness and hate. He made no answer, but I saw a smile, a smile of indefinable meaning, appear on his colourless lips that a moment after twitched convulsively. 'Do I not?' he said slowly, gasping, as if the words had been torn out of him by a supernatural power.

"I pulled the string of the whistle, and I did this because I saw the pilgrims on deck getting out their rifles with an air of anticipating a jolly lark. At the sudden screech there was a movement of abject terror through that wedged mass of bodies. 'Don't! don't you frighten them away,' cried some one on deck disconsolately. I pulled the string time after time. They broke and ran, they leaped, they crouched, they swerved, they dodged the flying terror of the sound. The three red chaps had fallen flat, face down on the shore, as though they had been shot dead. Only the barbarous and superb woman did not so much as flinch, and stretched tragically her bare arms after us over the sombre and glittering river.

"And then that imbecile crowd down on the deck started their little fun, and I could see nothing more for smoke.

"The brown current ran swiftly out of the heart of darkness, bearing us down towards the sea with twice the speed of our upward progress; and Kurtz's life was running swiftly too, ebbing, ebbing out of his heart into the sea of inexorable time. The manager was very placid, he had no vital anxieties now, he took us both in with a comprehensive and satisfied glance: the 'affair' had come off as well as could be wished. I saw the time approaching when I would be left alone of the party of 'unsound method.' The pilgrims looked upon me with disfavour. I was, so to speak, numbered with the dead. It is strange how

I accepted this unforeseen partnership, this choice of nightmares forced upon me in the tenebrous land invaded by these mean and greedy phantoms.

"Kurtz discoursed. A voice! a voice! It rang deep to the very last. It survived his strength to hide in the magnificent folds of eloquence the barren darkness of his heart. Oh, he struggled! he struggled! The wastes of his weary brain were haunted by shadowy images now—images of wealth and fame revolving obsequiously round his unextinguishable gift of noble and lofty expression. My Intended, my station, my career, my ideas—these were the subjects for the occasional utterances of elevated sentiments. The shade of the original Kurtz frequented the bedside of the hollow sham, whose fate it was to be buried presently in the mould of primeval earth. But both the diabolic love and the unearthly hate of the mysteries it had penetrated fought for the possession of that soul satiated with primitive emotions, avid of lying fame, of sham distinction, of all the appearances of success and power.

"Sometimes he was contemptibly childish. He desired to have kings meet him at railway stations on his return from some ghastly Nowhere, where he intended to accomplish great things. 'You show them you have in you something that is really profitable, and then there will be no limits to the recognition of your ability,' he would say. 'Of course you must take care of the motives—right motives—always.' The long reaches that were like one and the same reach, monotonous bends that were exactly alike, slipped past the steamer with their multitude of secular trees looking patiently after this grimy fragment of another world, the forerunner of change, of conquest, of trade, of massacres, of blessings. I looked ahead—piloting. 'Close the shutter,' said Kurtz suddenly one day; 'I can't bear to look at this.' I did so. There was a silence. 'Oh, but I will wring your heart yet!' he cried at the invisible wilderness.

"We broke down—as I had expected—and had to lie up for repairs at the head of an island. This delay was the first thing that shook Kurtz's confidence. One morning he gave me a packet of papers and a photograph—the lot tied together with a shoe-string. 'Keep this for me,' he said. 'This noxious fool' (meaning the manager) 'is capable of prying into my boxes when I am not looking.' In the afternoon I saw him. He was lying on his back with closed eyes, and I withdrew quietly, but I heard him mutter, 'Live rightly, die, die . . .' I listened. There was nothing more. Was he rehearsing some speech in his sleep, or was it a fragment of a phrase from some newspaper article? He had been writing for the papers and meant to do so again, 'for the furthering of my ideas. It's a duty.'

"His was an impenetrable darkness. I looked at him as you peer down at a man who is lying at the bottom of a precipice where the sun never shines. But I had not much time to give him, because I was helping the engine-driver to take to pieces the leaky cylinders, to straighten a bent connecting-rod, and in other such matters. I lived in an infernal mess of rust, filings, nuts, bolts, spanners, hammers, ratchet-drills—things I abominate, because I don't get on with them. I tended the little forge we fortunately had aboard; I toiled wearily in a wretched scrap-heap—unless I had the shakes too bad to stand.

"One evening coming in with a candle I was startled to hear him say a little tremulously, 'I am lying here in the dark waiting for death.' The light was within a foot of his eyes. I forced myself to murmur, 'Oh, nonsense!' and stood over him as if transfixed.

"Anything approaching the change that came over his features I have never seen before, and hope never to see again. Oh, I wasn't touched. I was fascinated. It was as though a veil had been rent. I saw on that ivory face the expression of sombre pride, of ruthless power, of craven terror—of an intense and hopeless despair. Did he live his life again in every detail of desire, temptation, and surrender during that supreme moment of complete knowledge? He cried in a whisper at some image, at some vision—he cried out twice, a cry that was no more than a breath:

" 'The horror! The horror!'

"I blew the candle out and left the cabin. The pilgrims were dining in the mess-room, and I took my place opposite the manager, who lifted his eyes to give me a questioning glance, which I successfully ignored. He leaned back, serene, with that peculiar smile of his sealing the unexpressed depths of his meanness. A continuous shower of small flies streamed upon the lamp, upon the cloth, upon our hands and faces. Suddenly the manager's boy put his insolent black head in the doorway, and said in a tone of scathing contempt:

" 'Mistah Kurtz—he dead.'

"All the pilgrims rushed out to see. I remained, and went on with my dinner. I believe I was considered brutally callous. However, I did not eat much. There was a lamp in there—light, don't you know—and outside it was so beastly, beastly dark. I went no more near the remarkable man who had pronounced a judgment upon the adventures of his soul on this earth. The voice was gone. What else had been there? But I am of course aware that next day the pilgrims buried something in a muddy hole.

"And then they very nearly buried me.

"However, as you see, I did not go to join Kurtz there and then. I did not. I remained to dream the nightmare out to the end, and to show my loyalty to Kurtz once more. Destiny. My destiny! Droll thing life is—that mysterious arrangement of merciless logic for a futile purpose. The most you can hope from it is some knowledge of yourself—that comes too late—a crop of unextinguishable regrets. I have wrestled with death. It is the most unexciting contest you can imagine. It takes place in an impalpable greyness, with nothing underfoot, with nothing around, without spectators, without clamour, without glory, without the great desire of victory, without the great fear of defeat, in a sickly atmosphere of tepid scepticism, without much belief in your own right, and still less in that of your adversary. If such is the form of ultimate wisdom, then life is a greater riddle than some of us think it to be. I was within a hair's-breadth of the last opportunity for pronouncement, and I found with humiliation that probably I would have nothing to say. This is the reason why I affirm that Kurtz was a remarkable man. He had something to say. He said it. Since I had peeped over the edge myself, I understand better the meaning of his stare, that could not see the flame of the candle, but was wide enough to embrace the whole universe, piercing enough to penetrate all the hearts that beat in the darkness. He had summed up—he had judged. 'The horror!' He was a remarkable man. After all, this was the expression of some sort of belief; it had candour, it had conviction, it had a vibrating note of revolt in its whisper, it had the appalling face of a glimpsed truth—the strange commingling of desire and hate. And it is not my own extremity I remember best—a vision of greyness without form filled with physical pain, and a careless contempt for the evanescence of all things—even of this pain itself. No! It is his extremity that I seem to have lived through. True, he had made that last stride, he had stepped over the edge, while I had been permitted to draw back my hesitating foot. And perhaps in this is the whole difference; perhaps all the wisdom, and all truth, and all sincerity, are just compressed into that inappreciable moment of time in which we step over the threshold of the invisible. Perhaps! I like to think my summing-up would not have been a word of careless contempt. Better his cry—much better. It was an affirmation, a moral victory paid for by innumerable defeats, by abominable terrors, by abominable satisfactions. But it was a victory! That is why I have remained loyal to Kurtz to the last, and even beyond, when a long time after I heard once more, not his own voice, but the echo of his magnificent eloquence thrown to me from a soul as translucently pure as a cliff of crystal.

"No, they did not bury me, though there is a period of time which I remember mistily, with a shuddering wonder, like a passage through some inconceivable world that had no hope in it and no desire. I found myself back in the sepulchral city resenting the sight of people hurrying through the streets to filch a little money from each other, to devour their infamous cookery, to gulp their unwholesome beer, to dream their insignificant and silly dreams. They trespassed upon my thoughts. They were intruders whose knowledge of life was to me an irritating pretence, because I felt so sure they could not possibly know the things I knew. Their bearing, which was simply the bearing of commonplace individuals going about their business in the assurance of perfect safety, was offensive to me like the outrageous flauntings of folly in the face of a danger it is unable to comprehend. I had no particular desire to enlighten them, but I had some difficulty in restraining myself from laughing in their faces, so full of stupid importance. I daresay I was not very well at that time. I tottered about the streets—there were various affairs to settle—grinning bitterly at perfectly respectable persons. I admit my behaviour was inexcusable, but then my temperature was seldom normal in these days. My dear aunt's endeavours to 'nurse up my strength' seemed altogether beside the mark. It was not my strength that wanted nursing, it was my imagination that wanted soothing. I kept the bundle of papers given me by Kurtz, not knowing exactly what to do with it. His mother had died lately, watched over, as I was told, by his Intended. A clean-shaved man, with an official manner and wearing gold-rimmed spectacles, called on me one day and made inquiries, at first circuitous, afterwards suavely pressing, about what he was pleased to denominate certain 'documents.' I was not surprised, because I had had two rows with the manager on the subject out there. I had refused to give up the smallest scrap out of that package, and I took the same attitude with the spectacled man. He became darkly menacing at last, and with much heat argued that the Company had the right to every bit of information about its 'territories.' And, said he, 'Mr. Kurtz's knowledge of unexplored regions must have been necessarily extensive and peculiar—owing to his great abilities and to the deplorable circumstances in which he had been placed: therefore—' I assured him Mr. Kurtz's knowledge, however extensive, did not bear upon the problems of commerce or administration. He invoked then the name of science. 'It would be an incalculable loss if,' etc. etc. I offered him the report on the 'Suppression of Savage Customs,' with the postscriptum torn off. He took it up eagerly, but ended by sniffing at it with an air of contempt. 'This is not what we had a right to expect,' he remarked. 'Expect nothing else,' I said. 'There are only private letters.' He withdrew upon some threat of legal proceedings, and I saw him no more; but another fellow, calling himself Kurtz's cousin, appeared two days later, and was anxious to hear all the details about his dear relative's last moments. Incidentally he gave me to understand that Kurtz had been essentially a great musician. 'There was the making of an immense success,' said the man, who was an organist, I believe, with lank grey hair flowing over a greasy coat-collar. I had no reason to doubt his statement; and to this day I am unable to say what was Kurtz's profession, whether he ever had any—which was the greatest of his talents. I had taken him for a painter who wrote for the papers, or else for a journalist who could paint—but even the cousin (who took snuff during the interview) could not tell me what he had been—exactly. He was a universal genius—on that point I agreed with the old chap, who thereupon blew his nose noisily into a large cotton handkerchief and withdrew in senile agitation, bearing off some family letters and memoranda without importance. Ultimately a journalist anxious to know something of the fate of his 'dear colleague' turned up. This visitor informed me Kurtz's proper sphere ought to have been politics 'on the popular side.' He had furry straight eyebrows, bristly hair cropped short, an eyeglass on a broad ribbon, and, becoming expansive, confessed his opinion that Kurtz really couldn't write a bit—'but heavens! how that man could talk! He electrified large meetings. He had faith—don't you see?—he had the faith. He could get himself to believe anything—anything. He would have been a splendid leader of an extreme party.' 'What party?' I asked. 'Any party,' answered the other. 'He was an—an—extremist.' Did I not think so? I assented. Did I know, he asked, with a sudden flash of curiosity, 'what it was that had induced him to go out there?' 'Yes,' said I, and forthwith handed him the famous Report for publication, if he thought fit. He glanced through it hurriedly, mumbling all the time, judged 'it would do,' and took himself off with this plunder.

"Thus I was left at last with a slim packet of letters and the girl's portrait. She struck me as beautiful—I mean she had a beautiful expression. I know that the sunlight can be made to lie too, yet one felt that no manipulation of light and pose could have conveyed the delicate shade of truthfulness upon those features. She seemed ready to listen without mental reservation, without suspicion, without a thought for herself. I concluded I would go and give her back her portrait and those letters myself. Curiosity? Yes; and also some other feeling perhaps. All that had been Kurtz's had passed out of my hands: his soul, his body, his station, his plans, his ivory, his career. There remained only his memory and his Intended—and I wanted to give that up too to the past, in a way—to surrender personally all that remained of him with me to that oblivion which is the last word of our common fate. I don't defend myself. I had no clear perception of what it was I really wanted. Perhaps it was an impulse of unconscious loyalty, or the fulfilment of one of those ironic necessities that lurk in the facts of human existence. I don't know. I can't tell. But I went.

"I thought his memory was like the other memories of the dead that accumulate in every man's life—a vague impress on the brain of shadows that had fallen on it in their swift and final passage; but before the high and ponderous door, between the tall houses of a street as still and decorous as a well-kept alley in a cemetery, I had a vision of him on the stretcher, opening his mouth voraciously, as if to devour all the earth with all its mankind. He lived then before me; he lived as much as he had ever lived—a shadow insatiable of splendid appearances, of frightful realities; a shadow darker than the shadow of the night, and draped nobly in the folds of a gorgeous eloquence. The vision seemed to enter the house with me—the stretcher, the phantom-bearers, the wild crowd of obedient worshippers, the gloom of the forests, the glitter of the reach between the murky bends, the beat of the drum, regular and muffled like the beating of a heart—the heart of a conquering darkness. It was a moment of triumph for the wilderness, an invading and vengeful rush which, it seemed to me, I would have to keep back alone for the salvation of another soul. And the memory of what I had heard him say afar there, with the horned shapes stirring at my back, in the glow of fires, within the patient woods, those broken phrases came back to me, were heard again in their ominous and terrifying simplicity. I remembered his abject pleading, his abject threats, the colossal scale of his vile desires, the meanness, the torment, the tempestuous anguish of his soul. And later on I seemed to see his collected languid manner, when he said one day, 'This lot of ivory now is really mine. The Company did not pay for it. I collected it myself at a very great personal risk. I am afraid they will try to claim it as theirs though. H'm. It is a difficult case. What do you think I ought to do—resist? Eh? I want no more than justice.' . . . He wanted no more than justice—no more than justice. I rang the bell before a mahogany door on the first floor, and while I waited he seemed to stare at me out of the glassy panel—stare with that wide and immense stare embracing, condemning, loathing all the universe. I seemed to hear the whispered cry, 'The horror! The horror!'

"The dusk was falling. I had to wait in a lofty drawing-room with three long windows from floor to ceiling that were like three luminous and bedraped columns. The bent gilt legs and backs of the furniture shone in indistinct curves. The tall marble fireplace had a cold and monumental whiteness. A grand piano stood massively in a corner; with dark gleams on the flat surfaces like a sombre and polished sarcophagus. A high door opened—closed. I rose.

"She came forward, all in black, with a pale head, floating towards me in the dusk. She was in mourning. It was more than a year since his death, more than a year since the news came; she seemed as though she would remember and mourn for ever. She took both my hands in hers and murmured, 'I had heard you were coming.' I noticed she was not very young—I mean not girlish. She had a mature capacity for fidelity, for belief, for suffering. The room seemed to have grown darker, as if all the sad light of the cloudy evening had taken refuge on her forehead. This fair hair, this pale visage, this pure brow, seemed surrounded by an ashy halo from which the dark eyes looked out at me. Their glance was guileless, profound, confident, and trustful. She carried her sorrowful head as though she were proud of that sorrow, as though she would say, I—I alone know how to mourn for him as he deserves. But while we were still shaking hands, such a look of awful desolation came upon her face that I perceived she was one of those creatures that are not the playthings of Time. For her he had died only yesterday. And, by Jove! the impression was so powerful that for me too he seemed to have died only yesterday—nay, this very minute. I saw her and him in the same instant of time—his death and her sorrow—I saw her sorrow in the very moment of his death. Do you understand? I saw them together—I heard them together. She had said, with a deep catch of the breath, 'I have survived'; while my strained ears seemed to hear distinctly, mingled with her tone of despairing regret, the summing-up whisper of his eternal condemnation. I asked myself what I was doing there, with a sensation of panic in my heart as though I had blundered into a place of cruel and absurd mysteries not fit for a human being to behold. She motioned me to a chair. We sat down. I laid the packet gently on the little table, and she put her hand over it.... 'You knew him well,' she murmured, after a moment of mourning silence.

" 'Intimacy grows quickly out there,' I said. 'I knew him as well as it is possible for one man to know another.'

" 'And you admired him,' she said. 'It was impossible to know him and not to admire him. Was it?'

" 'He was a remarkable man,' I said unsteadily. Then before the appealing fixity of her gaze, that seemed to watch for more words on my lips, I went on, 'It was impossible not to—'

" 'Love him,' she finished eagerly, silencing me into an appalled dumbness. 'How true! how true! But when you think that no one knew him so well as I! I had all his noble confidence. I knew him best.'

" 'You knew him best,' I repeated. And perhaps she did. But with every word spoken the room was growing darker, and only her forehead, smooth and white, remained illumined by the unextinguishable light of belief and love.

" 'You were his friend,' she went on. 'His friend,' she repeated, a little louder. 'You must have been, if he had given you this, and sent you to me. I feel I can speak to you—and oh! I must speak. I want you—you who have heard his last words—to know I have been worthy of him.... It is not pride.... Yes! I am proud to know I understood him better than any one on earth—he told me so himself. And since his mother died I have had no one—no one—to—to—'

"I listened. The darkness deepened. I was not even sure whether he had given me the right bundle. I rather suspect he wanted me to take care of another batch of his papers which, after his death, I saw the manager examining under the lamp. And the girl talked, easing her pain in the certitude of my sympathy; she talked as thirsty men drink. I had heard that her engagement with Kurtz had been disapproved by her people. He wasn't rich enough or something. And indeed I don't know whether he had not been a pauper all his life. He had given me some reason to infer that it was his impatience of comparative poverty that drove him out there.

" '... Who was not his friend who had heard him speak once?' she was saying. 'He drew men towards him by what was best in them.' She looked at me with intensity. 'It is the gift of the great,' she went on, and the sound of her low voice seemed to have the accompaniment of all the other sounds, full of mystery, desolation, and sorrow, I had ever heard—the ripple of the river, the soughing of the trees swayed by the wind, the murmurs of the crowds, the faint ring of incomprehensible words cried from afar, the whisper of a voice speaking from beyond the threshold of an eternal darkness. 'But you have heard him! You know!' she cried.

" 'Yes, I know,' I said with something like despair in my heart, but bowing my head before the faith that was in her, before that great and saving illusion that shone with an unearthly glow in the darkness, in the triumphant darkness from which I could not have defended her—from which I could not even defend myself.

" 'What a loss to me—to us!'—she corrected herself with beautiful generosity; then added in a murmur, 'To the world.' By the last gleams of twilight I could see the glitter of her eyes, full of tears—of tears that would not fall.

" 'I have been very happy—very fortunate—very proud,' she went on. 'Too fortunate. Too happy for a little while. And now I am unhappy for—for life.'

"She stood up; her fair hair seemed to catch all the remaining light in a glimmer of gold. I rose too.

" 'And of all this,' she went on mournfully, 'of all his promise, and of all his greatness, of his generous mind, of his noble heart, nothing remains—nothing but a memory. You and I—'

" 'We shall always remember him,' I said hastily.

" 'No!' she cried. 'It is impossible that all this should be lost—that such a life should be sacrificed to leave nothing—but sorrow. You know what vast plans he had. I knew of them too—I could not perhaps understand—but others knew of them. Something must remain. His words, at least, have not died.'

" 'His words will remain,' I said.

" 'And his example,' she whispered to herself. 'Men looked up to him—his goodness shone in every act. His example—'

" 'True,' I said; 'his example too. Yes, his example. I forgot that.'

" 'But I do not. I cannot—I cannot believe—not yet. I cannot believe that I shall never see him again, that nobody will see him again, never, never, never.'

"She put out her arms as if after a retreating figure, stretching them black and with clasped pale hands across the fading and narrow sheen of the window. Never see him! I saw him clearly enough then. I shall see this eloquent phantom as long as I live, and I shall see her too, a tragic and familiar Shade, resembling in this gesture another one, tragic also, and bedecked with powerless charms, stretching bare brown arms over the glitter of the infernal stream, the stream of darkness. She said suddenly very low, 'He died as he lived.'

" 'His end,' said I, with dull anger stirring in me, 'was in every way worthy of his life.'

" 'And I was not with him,' she murmured. My anger subsided before a feeling of infinite pity.

" 'Everything that could be done—' I mumbled.

" 'Ah, but I believed in him more than any one on earth—more than his own mother, more than—himself. He needed me! Me! I would have treasured every sigh, every word, every sign, every glance.'

"I felt like a chill grip on my chest. 'Don't,' I said, in a muffled voice.

" 'Forgive me. I—I—have mourned so long in silence—in silence. ... You were with him—to the last? I think of his loneliness. Nobody near to understand him as I would have understood. Perhaps no one to hear....'

" 'To the very end,' I said shakily. 'I heard his very last words. ...' I stopped in a fright.

" 'Repeat them,' she murmured in a heart-broken tone. 'I want—I want—something—something—to—to live with.'

"I was on the point of crying at her, 'Don't you hear them?' The dusk was repeating them in a persistent whisper all around us, in a whisper that seemed to swell menacingly like the first whisper of a rising wind. 'The horror! The horror!'

" 'His last word—to live with,' she insisted. 'Don't you understand I loved him—I loved him—I loved him!'

"I pulled myself together and spoke slowly.

" 'The last word he pronounced was—your name.'

"I heard a light sigh and then my heart stood still, stopped dead short by an exulting and terrible cry, by the cry of inconceivable triumph and of unspeakable pain. 'I knew it—I was sure!'... She knew. She was sure. I heard her weeping; she had hidden her face in her hands. It seemed to me that the house would collapse before I could escape, that the heavens would fall upon my head. But nothing happened. The heavens do not fall for such a trifle. Would they have fallen, I wonder, if I had rendered Kurtz that justice which was his due? Hadn't he said he wanted only justice? But I couldn't. I could not tell her. It would have been too dark—too dark altogether...."

Marlow ceased, and sat apart, indistinct and silent, in the pose of a meditating Buddha. Nobody moved for a time. "We have lost the first of the ebb," said the Director suddenly. I raised my head. The offing was barred by a black bank of clouds, and the tranquil waterway leading to the uttermost ends of the earth flowed sombre under an overcast sky—seemed to lead into the heart of an immense darkness.

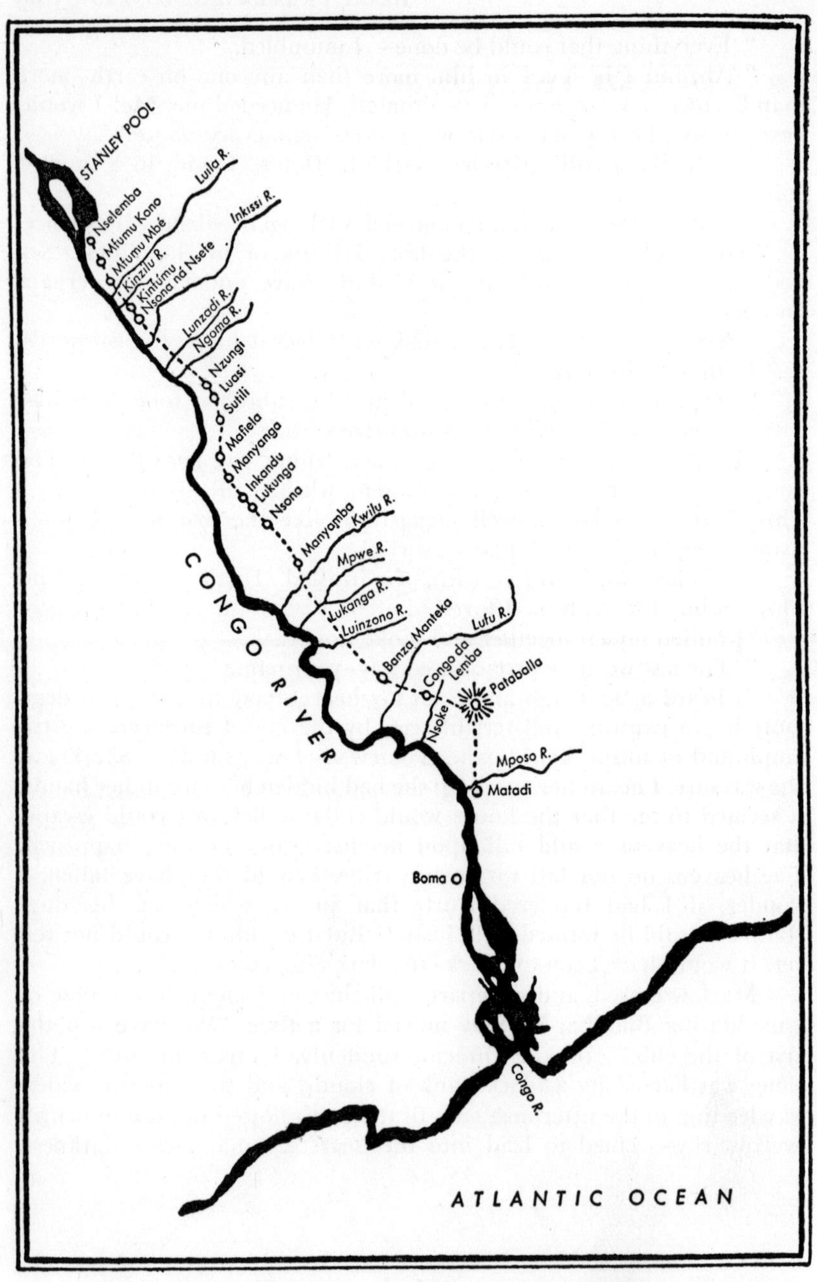

Rough Map of the route followed by Joseph Conrad on his overland journey in the Belgian Congo, from Matadi to Nselemba, in 1890; adapted from Last Essays.

CONRAD AND THE CONGO

THE CONGO DIARY*
Joseph Conrad

INTRODUCTION

The diary kept by Joseph Conrad in the Congo in 1890, or such of it as has survived (for there is no saying whether there was more or not), is contained in two small black penny notebooks, and is written in pencil. One carries his initials, J. C. K.—Joseph Conrad Korzeniowski. The first entry is dated 13 June, 1890, but in the second notebook dates are practically discarded, and it is impossible to say when the last entry was made. And names of places, also, are practically discarded in the second notebook, while abounding in the first, so that, though we can see that the diary was begun at Matadi, we cannot discover where it was ended. The last place mentioned is Lulanga, far up the great sweep of the Congo River to the north of the Equator, but there remain some twenty-four pages of the diary beyond that entry in which no name whatsoever appears. It must, indeed, have been continued into the very heart of that immense[231] darkness where the crisis of his story, *Heart of Darkness,* is unfolded. We know from *A Personal Record* that he reached ultimately somewhere to the neighbourhood of Stanley Falls; and Stanley Falls are farther from Lulanga than Lulanga is from Stanley Pool.

And it is in this same book that we can read how the Polish boy, when nine years of age, looking upon a map of Africa, had put his finger upon its unexplored centre, and had said to himself, "When I grow up I shall go *there.*" Go there he did, and these notebooks are the first expression of his fulfilled resolve.

The map will enable the reader to plot out, with reasonable accuracy, the exact route followed by Conrad on his overland journey, from Matadi, which is about one hundred miles above the mouth of the Congo, to Nselemba, on or near the south-east corner of Stanley Pool—a distance of probably more than two hundred and fifty miles

---

* Reprinted from *Last Essays* (London and Toronto: J. M. Dent and Sons, Ltd., 1926) with permission of the Trustees of the Joseph Conrad Estate, Doubleday & Co., Inc., New York, and J. M. Dent and Sons, Ltd., London. The introduction and the footnotes are by Richard Curle. Here, as throughout the volume, all cross-references to "Heart of Darkness" or "The Congo Diary" have been changed to conform with the pagination of the present volume.

from Matadi—where it was that he joined the *Roi des Belges,* as second in command, for the up-river voyage. The places and streams alluded to on this overland journey have been given on the map in Conrad's own spelling, even where their names have been altered (unless beyond recognition, which[232] may have happened in certain instances) in existing atlases, many of which have been examined, or can be only placed approximately, owing to their not being mentioned at all. The mapping of the Congo is not in a very advanced state, and, what with the paucity of the entries and the contradictory nature of the information, precise accuracy is not attainable. All the same, it is easy enough to trace the general line of his march, which lay much nearer the banks of the Congo than lies the railway which now runs between Matadi and Kinshasa on Stanley Pool.

The following is a reproduction of the first notebook alone—not, however, of the list of names, persons, books, stores, and the calculations that fill the last pages—consisting of thirty-two manuscript pages, not all of which are full, and twelve of which are further curtailed by Conrad's sectional drawings of the day's march. The given spelling and abbreviations have been adhered to throughout—they help to heighten its true flavour—but the paragraphing and the punctuation have been freely altered.

I may mention that these two notebooks are now preserved in the library of Harvard[233] University, and that when I was in America in 1925 I saw them again in their new and permanent home and checked the text once more.

As to the appended foot-notes, their chief purpose has been to show how closely some of the earlier pages of *Heart of Darkness* are a recollection of Conrad's own Congo journey. This story was serialised in *Blackwood's Magazine* between February and April 1899, and I remember Conrad telling me that its 40,000 words occupied only about a month in writing. When we consider the painful, slow labour with which he usually composed, we can perceive how intensely vivid his memories of this experience must have been, and, to judge from the parallel passages, how intensely actual. But then the notebook only goes to prove the almost self-evident contention that much of Conrad's work is founded upon autobiographical remembrance. Conrad himself wrote of this story in his Author's Note to the new edition of the *Youth* volume in which it appeared: "*Heart of Darkness* is quite as authentic in fundamentals as *Youth* . . . it is experience pushed a little (and only a little) beyond the actual facts of the case." If only he had kept a diary of his meeting and association with Kurtz![234]

The pages of Messrs. Dent's ordinary edition of *Youth* . . . which bear direct reference to the first volume of the diary, are only four, 75-78,[16-17, above] but in these few pages there are an astonishing number of touches strongly reminiscent of the diary. One would argue, indeed, that he must have consulted the diary when writing the story, but Mrs. Conrad assures me that it was not so. Twice had she saved it from the wastepaper basket, and probably by the time *Heart of Darkness* came to be written, Conrad had forgotten all about it, or did not dream that it had survived. He never spoke to me of it, and I never heard of its existence until after his death.

The second notebook, which is an entirely technical account of Congo navigation, written, no doubt, in relation to the then river charts, is not printed here, simply because it has no personal or literary interest. It is much longer than the first notebook, and is contained on seventy-nine pages, apart from several pages of rough outline maps. I reproduce a portion of one page, in order to show a sample:

> 11. N. (A) Long reach to a curved point. Great quantity of dangerous snags along the star[d] shore. Follow the slight bend of the shore with caution. The[235] Middle of the Channel is a S—B—[sand-bank] always covered. The more northerly of the two islands has its lower end bare of trees covered with grass and light green low bushes, then a low flat, and the upper end is timbered with light trees of a darker green tint.

It will be seen from this passage, which, though typical, is less technical than most, that the second notebook is not really, like the first, so much in the nature of a diary as of a specific aid to navigation. But those who recall the river journey in *Heart of Darkness,* with its dangers and its difficulties, will perceive how this notebook, too, has played its special and impersonal part in the construction of that story.

The title-page of the first notebook is almost all torn out, but the title-page of the second reads, "Up-river Book, commenced 3 August, 1890, S. S. *Roi des Belges.*" Long ago, when I was making, from Conrad's dictation, a list of the ships he had sailed in, he wrote opposite *Roi des Belges—"Heart of Darkness, Outpost."* And, in truth, hints for *Heart of Darkness,* reminders of *Heart of Darkness,* lie thick upon the pages of the first notebook, though *An Outpost of Progress*—"the lightest part of the loot I carried off from Central Africa," to quote his Author's Note to *Tales of Unrest,* in which it was published[236]—is only visible in the diary by the implication of the tropical African atmosphere.

No other diary of Conrad's is extant, and I am very sceptical as to whether he ever kept another. He was not at all that type of man, and his piercing memory for essentials was quite sufficient for him to recreate powerfully vanished scenes and figures for the purposes of his work. In 1890, of course, he had published nothing, and though we know that the unfinished MS. (seven chapters) of *Almayer's Folly* accompanied him on his Congo journey—*A Personal Record* describes how it was nearly lost on the river—yet it is doubtful whether he seriously envisaged its appearance in print at a future date. It was largely the breakdown of Conrad's health, due to this very trip, that caused him finally to abandon the sea, and if he had not abandoned the sea, how could he have become a novelist in the accepted sense? Unless we assume that genius must always find means of full expression—a big assumption and quite beyond proof—we owe it really to an accident that Conrad adopted writing as a career. Without this journey, and, therefore, without this diary, where would have been the great Conrad novels?[237]

Thirty-four years to a day from beginning the second notebook, Conrad died—3 August, 1924. Reading it again, I find, as I am continually finding, how many things there are which I would have liked to ask him and never did ask him, and how much I want to know which I never now can know. Well, that is always what happens when our friends depart. This diary is only a strange, tantalising fragment and must eternally remain so. Yet it has a value of its own, both real and romantic, and I am glad to be able to give it to the world.

Richard Curle.

The Diary

Arrived at Matadi[1] on the 13th of June, 1890.

Mr. Gosse, chief of the station (O.K.), retaining us for some reason of his own.

Made the acquaintance of Mr. Roger Casement,[2] which I should consider as a great pleasure under any circumstances and now it[238] becomes a positive piece of luck. Thinks, speaks well, most intelligent and very sympathetic.

Feel considerably in doubt about the future. Think just now that my life amongst the people (white) around here cannot be very comfortable. Intend avoid acquaintances as much as possible.

Through Mr. R. C. have made the acquain^{ce} of Mr. Underwood, the Manager of the English Factory (Hatton & Cookson) in Kalla Kalla. Av^{ge} com^{al}—hearty and kind. Lunched there on the 21st.

24th. Gosse and R. C. gone with a large lot of ivory down to Boma. On G.['s] return intend to start up the river. Have been myself busy packing ivory in casks. Idiotic employment. Health good up to now.

Wrote to Simpson, to Gov. B., to Purd.,[3] to Hope,[4] to Capt.

[1] On his voyage from Europe presumably.

[2] Afterwards the notorious Sir Roger Casement, who was hanged for treason on 3 August, 1916—the very date on which Conrad died eight years later. At this period Casement was in the employ of a commerical firm in the Congo. In 1898 he became British consul in the Congo Free State.

[3] Probably Captain Purdy, an acquaintance of Conrad.

[4] Conrad's old friend, now living in Essex, Mr. G. F. W. Hope. In 1900 Conrad dedicated *Lord Jim* to Mr. and Mrs. Hope, "with grateful affection after many years of friendship."

Froud,[5] and to Mar.[6] [239] Prominent characteristic of the social life here; people speaking ill of each other.[7]

Saturday, 28th June.

Left Matadi with Mr. Harou[8] and a caravan of 31 men.[9] Parted with Casement in a very friendly manner. Mr. Gosse saw us off as far as the State station.

First halt, M'poso. 2 Danes in Company.[10]

Sund[*ay*], *29th.*

Ascent of Pataballa sufficiently fatiguing. Camped at 11 a.m. at Nsoke river. Mosquitos [always spelt thus].

Monday, 30th.

To Congo da Lemba after passing black rocks. Long ascent. Harou giving up.[11] Bother.[240] Camp bad. Water far. Dirty. At night Harou better.

Tuesday, 1st July.

Left early in a heavy mist, marching towards Lufu river. Part route through forest on the sharp slope of a high mountain. Very long descent. Then market place from where short walk to the bridge (good) and camp. V. G. Bath. Clear river. Feel well. Harou all right. 1st chicken, 2 p.[m.] No sunshine to-day.

Wednesday, 2nd July.

Started at 5.30 after a sleepless night. Country more open. Gently undulating hills. Road good, in perfect order. (District of Lukungu.) Great market at 9.30. Bought eggs and chickens. Feel not well to-day. Heavy cold in the head. Arrived at 11 at Banza Manteka. Camped on the market place. Not well enough to call on the missionary. Water scarce and bad. Camp[g] place dirty. 2 Danes still in Company.

---

5 The then secretary of the London Ship-Masters' Society. See *A Personal Record* (Dent's reprint), p. 29: "Dear Captain Froud—it is impossible not to pay him the tribute of affectionate familiarity at this distance of years—had very sound views as to the advancement of knowledge and status for the whole body of the officers of the mercantile marine." [P. 7 in Kent edition. Ed.]

6 Probably Marguerite Poradowska, his aunt.

7 This was also a failing of the white men at the "Central Station" in *Heart of Darkness.*

8 Harou was an official of the Etat Indépendant du Congo Belge.

9 Compare *Heart of Darkness,* p. 16: "Next day I left that station at last with a caravan of 60 men for a 200-mile tramp." On thirteen out of the nineteen travelling days taken by Conrad on this overland journey he kept a record of the distance covered, and it totals 197½ miles.

10 Curiously enough, the identity of these two Danes was discovered by Monsieur G. Jean-Aubry in Brussels early in 1925. Not knowing that they were mentioned in the diary, he omitted to take names or particulars.

11 He seems to have been constantly unwell, and one may compare *Heart of Darkness,* p. 16: "I had a white companion too, not a bad chap, but rather too fleshy, and with the exasperating habit of fainting on the hot hillsides, miles away from the least bit of shade or water."

Thursday, 3rd July.

Left at 6 a.m. after a good night's rest. Crossed a low range of hills and entered a broad valley, or rather plain, with a break in the middle. Met an offer of the State inspecting. A few minutes[241] afterwards saw at a campg place the dead body of a Backongo. Shot?[12] Horrid smell.

Crossed a range of mountains, running N.W.–S.E. by a low pass. Another broad flat valley with a deep ravine through the centre. Clay and gravel. Another range parallel to the first-mentioned, with a chain of low foothills running close to it. Between the two came to camp on the banks of the Luinzono river. Campg place clean. River clear. Govt Zanzibari[13] with register. Canoe. 2 Danes campg on the other bank. Health good.

General tone of landscape grey-yellowish (dry grass) with reddish patches (soil) and clumps of dark green vegetation scattered sparsely about. Mostly in steep gorges between the high mountains or in ravines cutting the plain.[14][242]

Noticed Palma Christi–Oil Palm. Very straight, tall and thick trees in some places. Name not known to me. Villages quite invisible. Infer their existence from calbashes [*sic*] suspended to palm trees for the "Malafu." Good many caravans and travellers. No women, unless on the market place.

Bird notes charming. One especially a flutelike note. Another, kind of "boom" ressembling [*sic*] the very distant baying of a hound. Saw only pigeons and a few green parroquets. Very small and not many. No birds of prey seen by me.[15]

Up to 9 a.m. sky clouded and calm. Afterwards gentle breeze from the Nth generally and sky clearing. Nights damp and cool. White mists on the hills up about half way. Water effects very beautiful this morning. Mists generally raising before sky clears.

Distance 15 miles. General direction N.N.E.–S.S.W.

Friday, 4th July.

Left camp at 6 a.m. after a very unpleasant night. Marching across a chain of hills and then[243] in a maze of hills. At 8.15 opened out into an undulating plain. Took bearings of a break in the chain of

---

[12] Compare *Heart of Darkness,* p. 16: "Once a white man in an unbuttoned uniform camping on the path . . . was looking after the upkeep of the road, he declared. Can't say I saw any road or any upkeep, unless the body of a middle-aged negro with a bullethole in the forehead, upon which I absolutely stumbled three miles further on, may be considered as a permanent improvement."

[13] Compare *Heart of Darkness,* p. 16, in which he mentioned his meeting with a white man, who was accompanied by "an armed escort of lank Zanzibaris."

[14] In *Heart of Darkness,* p. 16, the country of the march is described as "a stamped-in network of paths spreading over the empty land, through long grass, through burnt grass, through thickets, down and up hilly ravines, up and down stony hills ablaze with heat."

[15] These natural history observations are curious, as Conrad practically never showed the slightest interest in such subjects.

mountains on the other side. Bearing N.N.E. Road passes through that. Sharp ascents up very steep hills not very high. The higher mountains recede sharply and show a low hilly country. At 9.30 market place. At 10 passed R. Lukanga and at 10.30 camped on the Mpwe R.

To-day's march. Direction N.N.E½.—N. Dist^{ce} 13 miles.

Saw another dead body lying by the path in an attitude of meditative repose.[16]

In the evening three women, of whom one albino, passed our camp; horrid chalky white with pink blotches; red eyes; red hair; features very negroid and ugly. Mosquitos. At night when the moon rose heard shouts and drumming in distant villages.[17] Passed a bad night.

Saturday, 5th July.

Left at 6.15. Morning cool, even cold, and very damp. Sky densely overcast. Gentle breeze from N.E. Road through a narrow plain up to[244] R. Kwilu. Swift flowing and deep, 50 yds. wide. Passed in canoes. After^{ds} up and down very steep hills intersected by deep ravines. Main chain of heights running mostly N.W.—S.E. or W. and E. at times. Stopped at Manyamba. Camp^{g} place bad—in a hollow—water very indifferent. Tent set at 10.15. N.N.E. Dist^{ce} 12 m.

To-day fell into a muddy puddle—beastly! The fault of the man that carried me. After camp^{g} went to a small stream, bathed and washed clothes. Getting jolly well sick of this fun.

To-morrow expect a long march to get to Nsona, 2 days from Manyanga. No sunshine to-day.

Sunday, 6th July.

Started at 5.40. The route at first hilly, then, after a sharp descent, traversing a broad plain. At the end of it a large market place. At 10 sun came out. After leaving the market passed another plain, then, walking on the crest of a chain of hills, passed 2 villages and at 11 arrived at Nsona. Village invisible.

Direction about N.N.E. Distance 18 miles.

In this camp (Nsona) there is a good camp^{g} place. Shady, water far and not very good. This[245] night no mosquitos owing to large fires, lit all round our tent. Afternoon very close: night clear and starry.

Monday, 7th July.

Left at 6, after a good night's rest, on the road to Inkandu, which

---

16 The most "Conradesque" phrase in the diary.

17 Compare *Heart of Darkness*, p. 16: "Perhaps on some quiet night the tremor of far-off drums, sinking, swelling, a tremor vast, faint; a sound weird, appealing, suggestive, and wild—and perhaps with as profound a meaning as the sound of bells in a Christian country."

is some distance past Lukunga Govt. station. Route very accidented.[18] Succession of round steep hills. At times walking along the crest of a chain of hills. Just before Lukunga our carriers took a wide sweep to the southward till the station bore Nth. Walking through long grass for 1½ hours. Crossed a broad river about 100 feet wide and 4 deep.

After another ½ hour's walk through manioc plantations in good order rejoined our route to the E^{d} of the Lukunga sta^{on}, walking along an undulating plain towards the Inkandu market on a hill. Hot, thirsty and tired. At 11 arrived on the m^{ket} place. About 200 people. Business brisk. No water; no camp^{g} place. After remaining for one hour left in search of a resting place. Row with carriers. No water. At last about 1½ p.m. camped on an exposed hill side near a[246] muddy creek. No shade. Tent on a slope. Sun heavy. Wretched.

Direction N.E. by N.—Distance 22 miles.

Night miserably cold. No sleep. Mosquitos.

Tuesday, 8th July.

Left at 6 a.m. About ten minutes from camp left main Gov^{t} path for the Manyanga track. Sky overcast. Rode up and down all the time, passing a couple of villages. The country presents a confused wilderness of hills, landslips on their sides showing red. Fine effect of red hill covered in places by dark green vegetation. ½ hour before beginning the descent got a glimpse of the Congo. Sky clouded.

To-day's march—3 h. General direction N. by E. Dist^{ce} 9½ miles.

Arrived at Manyanga at 9 a.m. Received most kindly by Messrs. Heyn and Jaeger. Most comfortable and pleasant halt.

Stayed here till the 25. Both have been sick. Most kindly care taken of us. Leave with sincere regrets.

Friday, the 25th July, 1890.

Left Manyanga at 2½ p.m. with plenty of hammock carriers. H. lame and not in very[247] good form. Myself ditto but not lame. Walked as far as Mafiela and camped—2 h.

Saturday, 26th.

Left very early. Road ascending all the time. Passed villages. Country seems thickly inhabited. At 11 arrived at large market place. Left at noon and camped at 1 p.m.

General direction E ½ N-W ½ S. Sun visible at 8 a.m. Very hot. Distance 18 miles.

Sunday, 27th.

Left at 8 a.m. Sent luggage carriers straight on to Luasi, and went ourselves round by the Mission of Sutili. Hospitable reception by Mrs. Comber. All the missio. absent. The looks of the whole establishment eminently civilized and very refreshing to see after the lots of tumbled down hovels in which the State & Company agents are content to live. Fine buildings. Position on a hill. Rather breezy.

[18] An odd Gallicism. Conrad knew French long before he knew English; moreover, he was naturally talking much French at this time.

Left at 3 p.m. At the first heavy ascent met Mr. Davis, Miss., returning from a preaching trip. Rev. Bentley away in the south with his wife. This being off the road, no section given.[19] [248]

Distance traversed about 15 miles. Gen. direction E.N.E.

At Luasi we get on again on to the Gov[t] road.

Camped at 4½ p.m. with Mr. Heche in company. To-day no sunshine. Wind remarkably cold. Gloomy day.

Monday, 28th.

Left camp at 6.30 after breakfasting with Heche. Road at first hilly. Then walking along the ridges of hill chains with valleys on both sides. The country more open and there is much more trees[20] growing in large clumps in the ravines.

Passed Nzungi and camped, 11, on the right bank of the Ngoma, a rapid little river with rocky bed. Village on a hill to the right.

General direction E.N.E.—Distance 14 miles.

No sunshine. Gloomy cold day. Squalls.

Tuesday, 29th.

Left camp at 7, after a good night's rest Continuous ascent; rather easy at first. Crossed wooded ravines and the river Lunzadi by a very decent bridge. At 9 met Mr. Louette escorting a sick agent of the comp[y] back to Matadi. Looking very well. Bad news from up the [249] river. All the steamers disabled—one wrecked.[21] Country wooded. At 10.30 camped at Inkissi.

General direction E.N.E.—Dist[ce] 15 miles.

Sun visible at 6.30. Very warm day.

Inkissi river very rapid; is about 100 yards broad. Passage in canoes. Banks wooded very densely, and valley of the river rather deep, but very narrow.

To-day did not set the tent, but put up in Gov[t] shimbek. Zanzibari[22] in charge—very obliging. Met ripe pineapple for the first time. On the road to-day passed a skeleton tied up to a post. Also white man's grave—no name—heap of stones in the form of a cross. Health good now.

Wednesday, 30th.

Left at 6 a.m. intending to camp at Kinfumu. Two hours' sharp walk brought me to Nsona na Nsefe. Market. ½ hour after Harou

---

19 Sections of the day's marches, with numerous names on them, were given under the following dates: 3, 4, 5, 6, 7, 8, 25, 28, 29, 30, 31 July, 1 August.

20 One of the few un-English phrases in the diary. By 1890 Conrad had been a British subject for six years, but he never learnt the language until he was grown up.

21 Compare *Heart of Darkness,* p. 17: "One of them [the white men at the Central Station] ... informed me with great volubility and many digressions ... that my steamer was at the bottom of the river."

22 See note 13.

arrived very ill with billious [*sic*] attack and fever. Laid him down in Gov^{t} shimbek.

Dose of ipec^{a}. Vomiting bile in enormous quantities. At 11 gave him 1 gramme of quinine[250] and lots of hot tea. Hot fit ending in heavy perspiration. At 2 p.m. put him in hammock and started for Kinfumu. Row with carriers all the way.[23] Harou suffering much through the jerks of the hammock. Camped at a small stream. At 4 Harou better; fever gone.

General direction N.E. by E. ½ E. Distance 13 miles.

Up till noon sky clouded and strong N.W. wind very chilling. From 1 p.m. to 4 p.m. sky clear and a very hot day. Expect lots of bother with carriers to-morrow. Had them all called and made a speech, which they did not understand.[24] They promise good behaviour.

Thursday, 31st.

Left at 6. Sent Harou ahead, and followed in ½ an hour.[25]

Road presents several sharp ascents, and a few others easier but rather long. Notice in places sandy surface soil instead of hard clay[251] as heretofore; think, however, that the layer of sand is not very thick and that the clay would be found under it. Great difficulty in carrying Harou. Too heavy—bother![26] Made two long halts to rest the carriers. Country wooded in valleys and on many of the ridges.

At 2.30 p.m. reached Luila at last, and camped on right bank. Breeze from S.W.

General direction of march about N.E. ½ E. Distance, est^{d} 16 miles.

Congo very narrow and rapid. Kinzilu rushing in. A short distance up from the mouth, fine waterfall. Sun rose red. From 9 a.m. infernally hot day. Harou very little better. Self rather seedy. Bathed. Luila about 60 feet wide. Shallow.

Friday, 1st of August, 1890.

Left at 6.30 a.m. after a very indifferently passed night. Cold, heavy mists. Road in long ascents and sharp dips all the way to Mfumu Mbé. After leaving there, a long and painful climb up a very steep hill; then a long descent to Mfumu Kono, where a long halt was made. Left at 12.30 p.m. towards Nselemba. Many ascents. The aspect of the

---

[23] Compare *Heart of Darkness,* p. 17: "Then he [the white man with him] got fever, and had to be carried in a hammock slung under a pole. As he weighed sixteen stone I had no end of rows with the carriers."

[24] Compare *Heart of Darkness,* p. 17: "... one evening, I made a speech in English with gestures, not one of which was lost to the sixty pairs of eyes before me."

[25] Compare *Heart of Darkness,* p. 17: "... the next morning I started the hammock off in front all right."

[26] Compare *Heart of Darkness,* p. 17: "... he [the white man with him] weighed sixteen stone. ..."

country entirely[252] changed. Wooded hills with openings. Path almost all the afternoon thro' a forest of light trees with dense undergrowth.

After a halt on a wooded hillside, reached Nselemba at 4.10 p.m. Put up at Gov[t] shanty. Row between the carriers and a man, stating himself in Gov[t] employ, about a mat. Blows with sticks raining hard. Stopped it.

Chief came with a youth about 13 suffering from gun-shot wound in the head. Bullet entered about an inch above the right eyebrow, and came out a little inside the roots of the hair, fairly in the middle of the brow in a line with the bridge of the nose. Bone not damaged apparently. Gave him a little glycerine to put on the wound made by the bullet on coming out.

Harou not very well. Mosquitos—frogs—beastly! Glad to see the end of this stupid tramp. Feel rather seedy. Sun rose red. Very hot day. Wind S[th].

General direction of march N.E. by N. Distance about 17 miles.[27] [253]

---

27 The journey from Matadi to this point by Stanley Pool took nineteen travelling days. Compare *Heart of Darkness,* p. 17: "On the fifteenth day I came in sight of the big river [Congo] again and hobbled into the Central Station."

IN THE HEART OF DARKNESS*

G. Jean-Aubry

> *The bitter knowledge that one gains from travel.*— Baudelaire
>
> *Land in a swamp, march through the woods, and in some inland post feel the savagery, the utter savagery, had closed round him—all that mysterious life of the wilderness that stirs in the forest, in the jungles, in the hearts of wild men.*—"Heart of Darkness"

He would have to start life all over again. No job in sight; a little money in his pocket: that was how things stood with Captain Kor-

---

* Reprinted from *The Sea Dreamer* by Gérard Jean-Aubry [trans. Helen Sebba], 1957, by permission of Doubleday & Co., Inc., New York, and George Allen & Unwin, Ltd., London. [Title mine. Ed.]

zeniowski when he took passage on a steamer bound for Europe in April, 1889. When he arrived in England early in June, it seems that he made a short visit to his friends, the Kliszczewskis, in Cardiff. The only reason he did not go straight to the Ukraine to see his uncle, as he had intended, was that after three years the Russian authorities had still not completed their formalities. The notice of his exemption from allegiance had just appeared in the *Official Gazette,* but Conrad still had to make an application to the governor of the province of his birth in order to set foot on imperial territory without difficulties.[149]

While he was waiting for the document that would permit him to go to Poland, since Thaddeus Bobrowski was prevented by his uncertain health and his limited means from going abroad to meet him, Conrad, giving up the rooms where he had always stayed before in North London, went to live in two furnished rooms in Bessborough Gardens, in the south of the city, not far from the Thames. There he lived for several months a life of leisure to which he had grown completely unaccustomed.

He had by no means given up the idea of going back to sea: but a command is not always to be had for the asking. Months went by and all his efforts came to nothing. He was in exactly the same situation as Marlow, the narrator of "Heart of Darkness":

> "I had then, as you remember, just returned to London after a lot of Indian Ocean, Pacific, China Seas—a regular dose of the East. . . . I began to look for a ship—I should think the hardest work on earth. But the ships wouldn't even look at me. And I got tired of that game too."

Days and months passed without bringing him the least hope of a command: the memory of the *Otago* was always in his heart. Captain Korzeniowski wandered about the town, went frequently to the City, either to the offices of Barr, Moering & Co. in Camomile Street where he would meet his friend Adolf Krieger, or to Fenchurch Street where he would go to see if Captain Froud, the helpful secretary of the Shipmasters' Society, had managed to hunt him up a ship.

Days and months passed; the summer was almost over and Captain Korzeniowski was still navigating "without maps or compass" in the streets of London. After roaming so many seas this novel kind of wandering was not altogether out of tune with his mood. Up to then he had lived entirely in the present: now, whether as a result of weariness, maturity, or an obsession with half-glimpsed scenes, this thirty-two-year-old captain fell to daydreaming.[150] The eager adventurous carelessness of his early youth was giving way to a mood of reminiscence, not about theories and systems, but about human beings, seen, sensed, or spoken to for a brief moment, whose faces, gestures, desires, and illusions he was able to re-create in these days of indolence in London.

One morning in September, "an autumn day with an opaline atmosphere, a veiled, semi-opaque, lustrous day ... one of those London days that have charm of mysterious amenity, of fascinating softness," in his furnished room in Bessborough Gardens, the captain got up from table after breakfast, pushed his chair back, and rang the bell resolutely, contrary to his usual habit which was to dawdle over his breakfast. The landlady's daughter appeared, surprised.

"Will you please clear away all this at once?" asked the captain in a final but perfectly calm tone. He was not at all sure that he wanted to write, that he meant to write, or that he had anything to write about. He heard her put the tray down in the passage and shut the door, and he went on smoking and looking out of the window. Then, at the urging of a sudden incomprehensible impulse, he put down his pipe, took a pen and "thinking of nothing whatever," began to write the story of Almayer's illusions.[1]

Never did a writer's life begin so late or so casually. If it was true that on that morning in September, 1889, Captain Korzeniowski began to make way for the novelist Joseph Conrad, he himself was far from suspecting it and far from desiring it. He said himself in *A Personal Record:*

> I never made a note of a fact, of an impression, or of an anecdote in my life. The conception of a planned book was entirely outside my mental range when I sat down to write; the ambition of being an author had never turned up amongst these gracious imaginary existences one creates fondly for oneself at times in the stillness and immobility of a daydream; yet it stands clear as the sun at noonday that from the moment I had done blackening over the first manuscript page of *Almayer's Folly* (it contained about two hundred words and this proportion of words to a page has remained[151] with me through the fifteen years of my writing life), from the moment I had, in the simplicity of my heart and the amazing ignorance of my mind, written that page the die was cast. Never had Rubicon been more blindly forded, without invocation to the gods, without fear of men.

Every morning of that misty London autumn Captain Korzeniowski pursued the memory of those tropical scenes, but, haunted as he was—despite himself—by Almayer's misfortunes, his main concern was still his maritime career. He had not the least idea of giving up the sea. For fifteen years he had owed the sea his livelihood—meager as it was and—as we have seen—strongly seasoned with dangers and risks; he felt he had been born to it. Besides, the profits he had accumulated during his year's command of the *Otago* were not substantial enough to allow him to contemplate a very long stay ashore. In any case, what would he have done ashore for any length of time? He had only a tiny group of friends in London: the Kriegers, a former master mariner named Hope and his wife, a few passing acquaintances. He had no

1 See *A Personal Record* (p. 69).

home, nothing but temporary lodgings. He thought only of getting away.

His friend Adolf Krieger had had him taken on as supercargo by the Antwerp shipowners, Walford & Co., who offered him some prospects of a voyage as captain to the West Indies and New Orleans, but that command, too, was a long time coming. Conrad's situation and his mood are both attributed to Marlow at the beginning of "Heart of Darkness":

"... I have a lot of relations living on the Continent, because it's cheap and not so nasty as it looks, they say. I am sorry to own I began to worry them. . . . I, Charlie Marlow, set the women to work—to get a job. Heavens! Well, you see, the emotion drove me. . . ."[152]

Of all the notions that might have come into the head of a captain of sailing ships, Conrad had suddenly been seized by the most unexpected, the most incomprehensible: to go to the Congo and command a wretched little steamboat of a few tons, a sardine can with a stern wheel. Many years ago, when he was a very little boy in Poland, he had announced that he would go to the heart of Africa:

It was in 1868, when nine years old or thereabouts, that while looking at a map of Africa of the time and putting my finger on the blank space then representing the unsolved mystery of that continent, I said to myself, with absolute assurance and an amazing audacity which are no longer in my character now:

"When I grow up I shall go *there*."

And of course I thought no more about it till after a quarter of a century or so an opportunity offered to go there—as if the sin of childish audacity was to be visited on my mature head.[2]

Perhaps, as Conrad makes Marlow say, a map of the Congo seen in a bookseller's window in Fleet Street stirred up these childhood desires. Perhaps a change in his relations with the Antwerp shipowners played a role in this unexpected move. In any case, at the end of September a letter from G. de Baerdemacker, shipbroker in Ghent, recommended Captain Korzeniowski to Mr. Albert Thys, staff captain, aide-de-camp to King Leopold, and managing director of the Société Anonyme Belge pour le Commerce du Haut-Congo at Brussels. "This gentleman," stated the letter, "is very warmly recommended to me by friends in London. Besides being a past master of his profession and holding the highest certificates, his general education is superior to that of most seamen[153] and he is a perfect gentleman." Early in November Joseph Conrad presented himself at the office of this Brussels company.

In 1889 the Congo was very much in the foreground. Since September, 1875, when King Leopold had founded the International As-

---

[2] Ibid., p. 13.

sociation for the Civilization of Central Africa, and since Stanley's expedition from Zanzibar to the Lower Congo in 1876 and 1877, Africa had aroused at once the most ardent interest and the most violent greed. A few months earlier, on February 17, 1889, Stanley, repeating the exploits of his search for Livingstone, had discovered and joined Emin Pasha in Kavali's camp. Scientific, journalistic, and political circles in Europe had followed these excursions with attentive and breathless interest. Brussels had become a focus of adventure. The daredevils of the whole world met there, as well as the missionaries. Men of good will and rogues came there to enter into contracts which would enable them to make use of their faith, talents, energy, greed, violence, or even their innocence, in the heart of what Stanley had called the "Dark Continent." England and Belgium were at that very moment getting ready to give Stanley a hero's welcome.

This atmosphere of adventure and discovery had reawakened in Conrad the geographical passions of his childhood. The young captain's imagination was still lively enough to flare up. He suddenly took it into his head to command one of the little steamboats of the Upper Congo. Conrad's impulses, as we have seen, were often no less obstinate than urgent.

They needed a captain who could speak French. Captain Korzeniowski met this requirement perfectly. The impression he made on Albert Thys must have been satisfactory, because there and then Thys promised him a job in the Congo as soon as there was a vacancy in the company's fleet.

The Société Anonyme Belge pour le Commerce du Haut-Congo was still comparatively new; in its permanent form it had existed only since December 10 of the year before; but under the direction of enterprising men this commerical venture was about to expand considerably. New stations were soon to be set up; new steamers built; plans were being studied for the possible layout of a railroad from Matadi to Stanley Pool, which would establish rapid communication between the two navigable stretches of the Congo. New perspectives were opening up for adventurous undertakings.[154]

The captain hurriedly broke his connections, such as they were, with Walford & Co. of Antwerp, but a final reply from Brussels still did not come. He grew impatient and, for want of anything else to do while he was waiting, he went on with *Almayer's Folly*. Meanwhile, Uncle Thaddeus, hearing that he was going to Brussels, reminded him that he had a relative there, a distant cousin, Alexander Poradowski, whom he had known long ago in Cracow.

In the middle of January, 1890, Conrad, thinking that this relative in Brussels might perhaps have some connections that would help to speed up his appointment, wrote to him in Polish that he expected to return to Brussels and would be happy to see him again, for he had not forgotten the kindness he had shown him long ago in Poland. He added that he would also be happy to make the acquaintance of his aunt, whom he knew only from a photograph which Alexander Poradowski had once shown him in Cracow.

Alexander Poradowski, cousin of Conrad's maternal grandmother, had fled to Brussels after the failure of the insurrection of 1863. He had later married a Frenchwoman from Lille, the daughter of a man with a high reputation in the scientific world, Émile Gachet, a philologist and paleographer. Madame Marguerite Poradowska, who was then about thirty, was very pretty and quick-witted and had created around her in Brussels a circle of friends and admirers. She had lived with her husband in Galicia for several years, and two years previously had published in the *Revue des Deux Mondes* a sketch of Ruthenian life in the form of a novel entitled *Yaga,* and a year later in the same periodical a novel of Polish life *Demoiselle Micia.* Uncle Thaddeus had kept his nephew informed of this latest literary distinction in the family.

Alexander Poradowski hastened to reply to his young cousin, restored to him from the bosom of the sea, but only to say that he was ill and was soon to have an operation and would therefore not be able to see him in March, as Conrad suggested. Conrad therefore decided to go to Brussels on his way to the Ukraine instead of on his way back, and left London on February 5. He arrived in Brussels that same evening. Two days later the uncle, whom he had not seen for sixteen or seventeen years, died.

In spite of the sad circumstances in which he had met his aunt, of whose existence he had known nothing, Conrad was by no means[155] blind to her charm and lively intelligence. During the two days he spent there, the captain had time to confide some of his ambitions to Madame Poradowska and she, impressed with the personality of this nephew, promised to do all she could for him. Their conversations and promises were interrupted by the sudden death of Alexander Poradowski. Conrad left Brussels before the funeral, taking with him a copy of Madame Poradowska's first novel. On February 11 he was in Warsaw. After an absence of sixteen years the prodigal son was on his way back to his native land for the first time.

Whether due to the sad ending of his stay in Brussels or the impression made on him by Madame Poradowska or by her novel *Yaga,* the traveler forgot one of his bags at the restaurant in the Friedrichstrasse station in Berlin. If it had not been for the watchfulness of a worthy and intelligent *Kofferträger,* he might have lost it for ever. The bag contained the first seven chapters of *Almayer's Folly.*

Conrad spent two days in Warsaw, where he had not been since his earliest childhood. Uncle Thaddeus must have alerted his relatives and friends to the mariner's return. An evening at a sporting club, where he was taken by a childhood friend, suddenly plunged the visitor into an atmosphere of patriotic talk and speculation such as he had not experienced for many a year.

From Warsaw and then from Lipovetz, where his uncle had sent a carriage and a servant to meet him, Joseph Conrad wrote in French to his new aunt. He apologizes for his style: "These badly written thoughts spring from the heart which knows neither the grammar nor the spelling of studied commiseration."[3] He stopped at Lublin, where his Zagórski cousins lived. He told them about the death of their uncle Alexander and from this family, with whom Madame Poradowska was very popular, he learned some new details about his French aunt, to whom he wrote that he had read her book twice during his journey.

It was at least eight hours by carriage from the railway station to Kazimierowka. While the traveler who had got off the train was dining, served by a Hebrew waiter, in an enormous barnlike bedroom, the door opened and, in a traveling costume of long boots, big sheepskin cap and a short coat girt with a leather belt, appeared[156] the confidential servant of Mr. Thaddeus Bobrowski, his mustache gleaming with little icicles, for it was bitterly cold outside. He had come to take delivery of that queer traveler who, as they said down there in the Ukraine, had been to the ends of the earth and farther and who spoke goodness knows what foreign language. When he heard his master's odd nephew speaking the purest Polish, his initial anxiety gave way to astonishment.

The next morning, following his master's instructions, the majordomo wrapped the captain in an enormous bearskin traveling coat and took his seat protectively by his side, as though he were in charge of a little boy going off to school. On this wintry day, in a sledge drawn by four bay horses, harnessed two by two, to the jingling of bells, the captain set out for the distant home, isolated and still unknown to him, lying beyond this infinite stretch of snow-covered plain, good wheat land, gently undulating, with little clumps of dark trees scattered here and there in the hollows.[4]

Once more he sees the sun setting on the plain as he used to see it on his childhood journeys. It is twenty-three years since he saw the sun setting on that land. Night is falling. Lulled by the rapid even movement of the sledge, the captain gives himself over to childhood memories, while in the dusk vast unfenced fields glide by, with a cottage here and there. At last the lights of Kazimierowka shine out, and waiting on the threshold is Uncle Thaddeus, with a warm embrace for the nephew he has not seen since that too brief glimpse at Marienbad, ready to clasp to his generous temperate heart *"Monsieur le capitaine au long-cours de la marine marchande britannique."*

As we can imagine, the days went by quickly in the two months

3 Letter of February 14, 1890.

4 See *A Personal Record,* pp. 20-22.

the visitor spent with his uncle. The captain had to tell all about his voyages. The uncle, who had recently been working on his memoirs, described the family's past life—a melancholy past—and his loneliness, filled now with responsibility for his numerous wards, for his good judgment was so widely respected that he had been made guardian of many orphans in the vicinity.

To the record that the exact and scrupulous Thaddeus Bobrowski had kept since December 13, 1869, of his nephew's income and expenses, below the line on which three years earlier he had noted:[157] "Thus Mr. Conrad's progress to the estate of man has cost 17,454 rubles," he added these final lines:

> On February 16 you came to visit me at Kazimierowka and I take this opportunity of presenting you with this financial statement together with my cordial good wishes for your future success.

The next day he handed the captain this little "record book."

Early in March the captain was able to revisit the setting of his childhood memories. Accompanied by his uncle, he spent ten days on the estate at Nowofastov, some fifty miles away, where he lived as a little child and which Thaddeus Bobrowski had deeded to his sister-in-law, Madame Montrésor, after the death of his daughter. At Nowofastov relatives and friends listened, spellbound, to this born storyteller who was not reluctant to tell his tales.

Back at the Kazimierowka house there was a constant coming and going from one room to another. Late at night as he was going to bed, Conrad would hear his uncle's quick footsteps on the waxed floor of the next room, crossing the anteroom lined with bookshelves and entering the drawing room, where they became inaudible on the thick carpet. Through the closed blinds of his room, illuminated by two candelabra with four candles each, the visitor would hear the gentle sound of sleigh bells dying away beyond the village.

On a writing desk was lying, unostentatiously, a brown paper packet: the manuscript of *Almayer's Folly*. But how was he to work on it amid all these memories? Deep in this snow-covered Ukrainian plain the captain hardly gives a thought to the heavy scents of the tropical forest, to Almayer's vast hopes or his daily disappointments. Yet he thinks of Africa. For all his childhood memories, his uncle, his relatives, his friends, the captain does not lose sight of his African project. Moreover, his aunt in Brussels, in spite of her bereavement, has not forgotten her promises and has written that she is doing all she can. Her help is very useful, for letters arrive from London implying that Captain Korzeniowski's references have not satisfied the Société du Haut-Congo. "The prospect of seeing you in Brussels," he writes to Madame Poradowska after a month's absence, "will be a comfort to me when the time comes to leave my uncle." Their[158] liking is mutual. The young widow does not forget her literary pretensions; Conrad, the writer-to-be, lets himself go in letters in a serious vein. In the silence of the country house in the Ukraine, the English sea captain applies himself to exercises in French literature:

> Life rolls on in bitter waves like the dark, cruel ocean under a sky covered with sad clouds. There are days when it seems to the poor souls embarked on the hopeless voyage that no ray of sun has ever managed to pierce this dreary veil, that the sun will never shine again, that it has never even existed.
>
> Eyes which the biting wind of grief has filled with tears must be forgiven if they refuse to see the blue sky: lips which have tasted the bitterness of life must be forgiven if they refuse to utter words of hope. . . .[5]

Another letter from his Aunt Marguerite at the beginning of April gives him better news of his projects. The prodigal's taste for adventure revives; his taste for the fatted calf has not replaced his appetite for *la vache enragée*. He informs the Société du Haut-Congo that he will present himself at their offices toward the end of the month. On April 18 he takes leave of his uncle; on the twenty-second he is in Lublin, where he spends forty-eight hours with his Zagórski cousins, on the twenty-ninth he is in Brussels. He cannot afford to devote much time to the charms of his Poradowska aunt, for he is suddenly appointed captain and promised the command of one of the Upper Congo steamboats. He barely has time to go back to London to pack his belongings, buy a few articles, return to Brussels to sign his contract, go back to London, then to Brussels again to say good-by to his aunt. He leaves Brussels by train on May 11, 1889, for Bordeaux, where he takes passage for Boma on the *Ville de Maceio* belonging to the Compagnie des Chargeurs Réunis.

At the beginning of "Heart of Darkness" Marlow, who is Conrad himself, has this to say about the reasons for the company's sudden hurry to engage him as a captain:

> "I got my appointment—of course; and I got it very quick. It appears the Company had received news that one of their captains had been killed in a scuffle with the natives. . . . It[159] was only months and months afterwards, when I made the attempt to recover what was left of the body, that I heard the original quarrel arose from a misunderstanding about some hens. . . . Through this glorious affair I got my appointment, before I had fairly begun to hope for it. . . .

And then Marlow gives his unforgettable account of his visit to the company's office. The women dressed in black, knitting in the outer office like impassive Fates; the huge, many-colored map of Central Africa; the interview with the managing director which lasted only a few seconds; the compassionate secretary; the visit to the doctor; the farewells to his aunt—this succession of details and scenes, all extraor-

[5] Letter of March 23, 1890.

dinarily vivid and all bearing the imprint of a biting irony, are nothing but the memory of actuality.

Just before leaving London, in a letter to one of his first cousins, Madame Tyska, née Bobrowska, a letter intended for all his relations in Lublin, Joseph Conrad announced that he was leaving "for a stay of three years in the middle of Africa." In fact, he left more like someone who has taken himself at his own word than like an enthusiastic traveler. During the ship's call at Teneriffe, he wrote to Madame Poradowska:

> We left Bordeaux on a rainy day. A sad day; not a very cheerful departure. Haunting memories; vague regrets; hopes that are still more vague.[6]

And a few weeks later, on June 10, he writes to her again from Libreville. He speaks tenderly of his uncle and declares: "You have enriched my life with a new interest, a new affection." He asks her to write to him and adds: [160]

> If one could get rid of one's heart and memory (and brain, too) and then get a whole new set of these things, life would become ideally amusing. ... Pending the inevitable fever I am very well. ... After this I shall not be able to write until we get to Léopoldville. It takes twenty days to get there: on foot, too. Horrors!

The ship had called at Teneriffe, Dakar, Konakri, Sierra Leone, Grand-Bassam, Kotonu, Libreville, Loango, Banana at the mouth of the Congo, and Boma, the seat of the government of the Free State since 1886. All these ports of call explain why, after leaving Bordeaux on May 10, Captain Korzeniowski did not reach Boma until June 13. From there he went to Matadi in a little steamboat. His work was not to begin until he reached Stanley Pool, some two hundred and fifty miles away, above the rapids.

Conrad's traveling companion all the way from Bordeaux had been an agent of the Free State named Prosper Harou, who was going back to his station. This Belgian official, who had done several tours of duty in Africa, knew its dangers and did not hide from the newcomer the fact that actual circumstances were a little different from the official statistics. These revelations cast a slight pall over the journey, but the traveler tried to make the best of things, as we can see from a letter in Polish which he wrote on board the *Ville de Maceio* to his cousin Charles Zagórski:

> 22 May, 1890, Freetown, Sierra Leone.
>
> My very dear Charles,
>
> It is just a month today since you were horrified by my hasty departure from Lublin. You can see from the date and address of this letter that I had

---

[6] Letter of May 15, 1890.

to hurry. Only now am I beginning to breathe a bit more calmly. If you only knew what a confounded lot of things I had to see to. From London to Brussels, back to London; then back to Brussels again. You should have seen all the tin chests and revolvers, the high boots and the touching farewells. One more handshake and one more pair of trousers! And if you only knew how many bottles of medicine and affectionate wishes I am taking with me, you would understand the typhoon, cyclone, hurricane, earthquake—no! the universal cataclysm—the fantastic atmosphere of[161] shopping, business matters and sentimental leave-taking in which I spent two whole weeks! ... I shall be at Boma no doubt on the 7th of next month and then leave Boma with my caravan to go to Léopoldville. As far as I can make out from my contract letter, I am destined to command a steamboat belonging to Mr. Delcommune's exploring party, which is now getting under way. I am delighted at this prospect, but I don't know anything definite, because it seems that everything is supposed to be kept secret. What does worry me is that I have been told that 60% of the company's employees go back to Europe without even staying six months. ... Others are hastily sent back after a year so that they won't die in the Congo. Heaven forbid! That would spoil the statistics, which are excellent, you see! In brief, it seems that only 7% can stand three years' service. ... Ah yes, but a Polish gentleman, soaked in British tar! How that will confuse them! We shall see. In any case I can console myself by remembering that—faithful to our national traditions—I got myself into this of my own free will.

Obviously Conrad was no longer unaware of the risks of this adventure, though they had certainly not been put to him frankly in Brussels before his departure.

A little later, on June 24, Uncle Thaddeus wrote to his nephew from the Ukraine:

I am following you through space in my thoughts, wondering what is happening to you. I suppose that if you haven't yet been put on a spit and eaten broiled (or perhaps in a stew) I shall get a letter from you sooner or later. ... Your last letter is dated from Teneriffe, and according to my calculations you ought to be at Léopoldville by now. Don't wait to sum up your opinions on people and things and on the civilizing mission in which after all—confound it! you are a cog, but, while all that is crystallizing into sentences, tell me quickly how you are and what your first impressions are like.

And he ends another letter along the same lines as his nephew, though less philosophically and confidently.[162]

Your letter of May 28 was dated from Libreville, so it took seven weeks. You wrote it on the frontier of civilization and barbarism. What am I to expect if you go to the very heart of Africa, where the mail only arrives once a month? ... Your only consolation and your only hope of adding to your pertinacity and optimism in the present struggle for life will lie in Molière's famous phrase: *"Tu l'as voulu, George Dandin!"* I for my part will count the days and weeks of the three years that separate us no less impatiently, wondering if my carcass can hold out so long.

On June 18 the traveler writes to Madame Poradowska from Matadi:

> I leave tomorrow, on foot. No donkeys here, except your very humble servant. A twenty day caravan.

He did not leave the next day, not until ten days later. In 1890 Matadi was already a fairly important station; there were almost two hundred Europeans there and five or six trading stations of various nationalities. What gave Matadi new life and would rapidly increase its importance was that work had just begun on the Matadi-Kinchassa railway, which was to facilitate the rapid transport of goods from the Upper Congo to the ports of embarkation for Europe. At that time these goods all had to be carried on the backs of porters along caravan tracks.

Conrad's call at Matadi did nothing to raise his spirits. This part of the Congo looks like a lake surrounded on all sides by high mountains, but nature is not at her most attractive there, according to Captain Thys, the man whom Conrad had talked to in Brussels before leaving.

> When you arrive in Matadi (he wrote), you seem to have reached an accursed land, a real barrier erected by nature to impede progress.

Joseph Conrad cared little about fostering so-called progress, which he regarded with considerable scepticism, expressed later in "An Outpost of Progress" and "Heart of Darkness." His stay in[163] Matadi seemed endless, for he was impatient to start on the two-hundred-mile march that would take him to his ship.

One note he wrote about his stay in Matadi tells us a great deal about his impressions of the people he met in his first few days there:

> Think just now that my life amongst the people (white) around here cannot be very comfortable. Intend avoid acquaintances as much as possible.[7]

This sentence occurs at the beginning of a document which is quite exceptional in Conrad's life: a diary which he kept in English from June 13 to August 1, 1890, that is, for the period of his stay at Matadi and the long trek from Matadi to Kinchassa.

At all events, he made the acquaintance of the head of the station, a Belgian named Gosse, a former officer, who was to die six months later, and of another man, who subsequently attained an extraordinary notoriety, Mr.—afterward Sir—Roger Casement, who was then twenty-six and was in the Congo for the third time, currently with the Société Anonyme Belge. He was, in fact, one of the few people in

[7] *Last Essays,* "Congo Diary." (p. 74.)

Africa who made a good impression on Conrad: "Thinks, speaks well, most intelligent and very sympathetic," he wrote in his diary shortly after his arrival, and on leaving Matadi he notes again: "Parted with Casement in a very friendly manner."

While waiting to start, he passed the time as best he could in activities which had very little to do with his proper functions. "Have been busy packing ivory in casks. Idiotic employment." And the same day he notes again: "Prominent characteristic of the social life here: people speaking ill of each other." The atmosphere of this colonial outpost certainly did not appeal to him.

At last, on June 28, together with Prosper Harou, he left Matadi with a caravan of thirty-one porters. At their first halt, before crossing the river at M'poso, two Danish officials joined them and they all made the ascent of the mountainous Pataballa region together. The fatigue and unpleasantness can be imagined from what Captain Thys had written about this region a short time previously:

> If, on leaving Matadi you take the land route and head for M'poso and the Pataballa Range, the same impression continues:[164] and when you arrive at Pataballa, sweating and panting, your legs aching, there falls from your lips an exclamation which doubtless never varies: "What awful country!"

At the end of this long climb, toward Congo da Lemba, his traveling companion began to suffer from fainting spells which were to occur repeatedly during the journey so that he had to be carried most of the way. For eleven days, from Matadi to Manyanga, it was a monotonous march, at the rate of fifteen to twenty miles a day, along an uneven track, sometimes through forest, sometimes over a plain covered with tall grass—a weary and dismal expedition of which he has given this striking picture:

> "Paths, paths, everywhere; a stamped-in network of paths spreading over the empty land, through long grass, through burnt grass, through thickets, down and up chilly ravines, up and down stony hills ablaze with heat; and a solitude, a solitude, nobody, not a hut."[8]

They would start very early in the morning on a tiring march which lasted until eleven o'clock, along a track broken now and again by a native market or a river to be forded or crossed by means of a bridge of lianas. Once they met an officer of the Free State on a tour of inspection and a few minutes later saw the body of a Negro who had been shot. Pitch camp, cook, sleep, strike camp, and off again. They marched through gray-yellowish country "with reddish patches (soil) and clumps of dark green vegetation scattered sparsely about." They

---

8 "Heart of Darkness." (p. 16.)

marched through steep gorges or along the crest of a mountain chain. The nights were damp and cold, the mornings misty, the middle of the day scorching. The camp sites were dirty, the water often brackish, and the mosquitoes kept up their activity night and day. Often there was an argument with the porters just before setting out. After a week of this, Conrad notes in his diary: "Getting jolly well sick of this fun."

At last, on the morning of July 8, they arrived at Manyanga. They were very kindly received there by the director of the Transport Company of the Upper Congo, an Englishman, Reginald Heyn, and his assistant, Jaeger.

Up to now Conrad's health had been satisfactory. During his stay[165] at Manyanga he fell ill, probably with an attack of fever. Harou's health was no better.

After a sixteen-day rest, they set off again in a rather poor state and resumed their march day after day, during which the noonday heat was rivaled by the dangerous coolness of the nights.

On Sunday, July 27, they spent the day at the Sutili mission station, where they were received by the missionary's young wife, Mrs. Annie Comber. Little did Conrad suspect that on that very day, far away at Luri in Corsica, Dominic Cervoni, his master in seamanship and the comrade of his Mediterranean years, was dying, at the age of fifty-six, after thirty-seven years in the service of the sea.

The march continued, monotonous as ever, except for an occasional skeleton tied to a stake or a heap of stones in the form of a cross marking the grave of a white man. Harou was seriously ill with one attack of fever after another and had to be carried again. He was heavy; the porters complained and deserted at night with their loads. Conrad had to use his authority to put down the beginnings of a mutiny. After nine days they arrived somehow or other, limping and stumbling, at Kinchassa, the home port of the Upper Congo flotilla.

There the company had set up a shipyard, or rather an assembly yard. It was there that they assembled the shells of ships sent out in sections from Europe and carried on men's backs from Matadi to the Pool. Damaged ships were also repaired there.

When Conrad arrived they were at work on repairs to the ship intended for him, the *Florida,* for she had been wrecked a few days previously. Captain Korzeniowski did not, however, have to wait two months for them to repair his ship, as Marlow did in "Heart of Darkness." He embarked as second officer that same day on a little steamboat of fifteen tons, the *Roi des Belges.* Captain Koch, a Dane who had been upriver several times, undertook to initiate him into the difficulties and dangers of this fresh-water navigation. Arriving in Kinchassa on August 2, he left the next day, as the manuscript heading of a second diary proves: "Up River Book, commenced 3rd August, 1890, S.S. *Roi des Belges.*"

In Kinchassa he got in touch with Camille Delcommune, temporary acting manager, whom he calls "the manager" in "Heart of Darkness": [166]

"My first interview with the manager was curious. He did not ask me to sit down after my twenty-mile walk that morning. He was commonplace in complexion, in feature, in manners, and in voice. . . . He had no genius for organizing, for initiative, or for order even. That was evident in such things as the deplorable state of the station. He had no learning, and no intelligence. His position had come to him—why? Perhaps because he was never ill . . ."

We shall refer later to an impression of this same Camille Delcommune which occurs in Conrad's own correspondence and confirms this one.

On August 4 the S.S. *Roi des Belges,* carrying Camille Delcommune, Captain Koch and Captain Korzeniowski, the agents Keyaerts, Rollin, and Van der Heyden, and the engineer Gossens, left Kinchassa with two lighters and two native canoes in tow. On August 26 the ship reached the confluence of the Ubangi; on September 1 she arrived at her destination, Stanley Falls, only twenty-eight days after her departure from Stanley Pool. This voyage, which in those days was considered remarkably quick, must have seemed interminable to Conrad, for he says in "Heart of Darkness": "It was just two months from the date we left the creek when we came to the bank below Kurtz's station."

Nothing could give a more vivid feeling of this thousand-mile trip up the Congo aboard that wretched little fifteen-ton steamboat than the series of admirable descriptions that make up the greater part of "Heart of Darkness," from which we quote the following passage:

"Going up that river was like traveling back to the earliest beginnings of the world, when vegetation rioted on the earth and the big trees were kings. An empty stream, a great silence, an impenetrable forest. The air was warm, thick, heavy, sluggish. . . .[167]

The ship did not stay long at Stanley Falls and there is in "Heart of Darkness" no description of this farthest point of navigation on the river, but another page from the writer's work gives us an impression of Captain Korzeniowski in the heart of Africa. In it we find an echo of the feeling of solitude that came over him at this time, which was due not only to his being plunged into a mysterious silence, "into the heart of an immense darkness," but also to the fact[168] that he no longer felt between his white companions and himself that innate solidarity, that common conception of human dignity, that fidelity to a few very simple and, so to speak, tacitly assumed principles which throughout his childhood and his fifteen years at sea had been the constant atmosphere of his life and, at the bottom of his heart, his safeguard and his pride.

Everything was dark under the stars. Every other white man on board was asleep. I was glad to be alone on deck, smoking the pipe of peace after an anxious day. The subdued thundering mutter of the Stanley Falls hung in the heavy night air of the last navigable reach of the Upper Congo, while no more than ten miles away, in Reshid's camp just above the Falls, the yet unbroken power of the Congo Arabs slumbered uneasily. Their day was over. Away in the middle of the stream, on a little island nestling all black in the foam of the broken water, a solitary little light glimmered feebly, and I said to myself with awe, "This is the very spot of my boyish boast."

A great melancholy descended on me. Yes, this was the very spot. But there was no shadowy friend to stand by my side in the night of the enormous wilderness, no great haunting memory, but only the unholy recollection of a prosaic newspaper "stunt" and the distasteful knowledge of the vilest scramble for loot that ever disfigured the history of human conscience and geographical exploration. What an end to the idealized realities of a boy's daydreams! I wondered what I was doing there, for indeed it was only an unforeseen episode, hard to believe in now, in my seaman's life. Still, the fact remains that I have smoked a pipe of peace at midnight in the very heart of the African continent, and felt very lonely there.[9]

The purpose of the voyage of the *Roi des Belges* from Kinchassa to Stanley Falls was to relieve one of the company's agents at the Falls whose health was causing the greatest anxiety. This explains the haste of the steamboat's departure from Kinchassa and its passage upriver.

This dying agent, whom Conrad turned into the abominable hero[169] of "Heart of Darkness," Kurtz, actually had quite a similar name, Georges-Antoine Klein. He had arrived in the Congo late in 1888 and was put in charge of the company's station at Stanley Falls in 1890. He died on September 21 aboard the S.S. *Roi des Belges* and was buried at Bolobo by the ship's company.

It is impossible without formal proof to be sure of the exact resemblance between Kurtz and Klein, but it is beyond doubt, when one is familiar with Conrad's habit of using in his work elements drawn from reality, that these two characters, one real, the other fictitious, were alike in more than name.[10]

Going upriver Captain Korzeniowski was only the first mate of the *Roi des Belges* but he brought the steamer back to Kinchassa as captain, as the following letter shows:

---

[9] *Last Essays*, "Geography and Some Explorers." (pp. 24-25.)

[10] This is confirmed by an examination of the manuscript of "Heart of Darkness" now in the library of Yale University. On p. 55 of this manuscript Conrad had written: "In the interior you will no doubt meet Monsieur Klein. . . ." He later crossed out the last two words and changed them to Mr. Kurtz, a correction he repeated in three other places in the same paragraph. (Note from Mr. John Gordan, Harvard University, November 11, 1938.) [See p. 167, below.]

SOCIÉTÉ ANONYME BELGE
POUR LE COMMERCE DU HAUT-CONGO
9, rue Brèderode.
Stanley Falls, Sept. 6, 1890

Mr. Conrad Korzeniowski,
Captain.

I have the honor to ask you to take over the command of the S.S. *Roi des Belges* as of today, until the recovery of Captain Koch.

Yours etc.
Camille Delcommune.

Thus Conrad owed his official command solely to Captain Koch's illness—a fact which will explain some later events.

This date, September 6, probably coincided with their departure from the Falls, since, due to the current, the passage back took only half as long as the trip upriver. In any case, the date of Klein's burial[170] (September 21) must correspond to that of the ship's call at Bolobo. On September 24 the *Roi des Belges* returned to her base at Kinchassa and Conrad's one experience as a fresh-water mariner came to an end.

From "Heart of Darkness," which parallels so closely Conrad's own life at this period, we can assume that Captain Korzeniowski's relations with the manager had soon become cool and even somewhat strained. The captain's disappointment, his conviction that they wanted to keep him in a subordinate position and that the promises made in Brussels would never be fulfilled in the Congo, his growing discontent, his outright indignation at the hypocritical greed of these traders and their methods—all these feelings had been in evidence even before his meeting with Kurtz-Klein, which, as Marlow said, "seemed to shed a kind of light on all the things around him and on his own thoughts." Even before he left Kinchassa to go upriver, he had confided his first disappointments to his uncle, as the following reply clearly shows:

> Three days ago I received your letter from Stanley Pool. . . . I see that you are very angry with the Belgians, who are exploiting you unscrupulously. You must admit that this time nothing forced you to put yourself in the Belgians' hands. *"Tu l'as voulu, tu l'as voulu, George Dandin."* . . . If you had paid attention to my opinion in the whole business, you would have gathered, after our conversation, that I was not very keen on your project. As a Polish gentleman, I have always preferred what is safer and less brilliant to what is more brilliant and less safe. . . . If you break your contract, you risk expense and being accused of irresponsibility, which might harm your future career.[11]

Conrad did not need this advice from Thaddeus Bobrowski (which, in any case, did not reach him until long afterward) to per-

[11] Letter of September 14, 1890.

suade him to go ahead with the adventure he had so unfortunately engaged in. He was not going to give in. The day of his return to Kinchassa, in the course of a long letter to his cousin, Madame Tyska, he said: [171]

> I am very busy getting ready for a new expedition on the Kasai River. I think in a few days I shall leave Kinchassa again for several months, possibly more than ten months.

And two days later in a letter in French to Madame Poradowska he tells her that he is back from Stanley Falls, where he went "to learn the river." He adds:

> My days here are dreary. There is no doubt about it. I decidedly regret having come here: indeed, I regret it bitterly. Everything here repels me. Men and things, but especially the men. And I repel them, too. From the manager in Africa—who has taken the trouble of telling a lot of people that he can't stand me, down to the lowest mechanic—they all have the gift of getting on my nerves. . . .
>
> The manager is a common ivory-dealer with sordid instincts who considers himself a trader when he is nothing but a kind of African shopkeeper. His name is Delcommune. He hates the English, and of course I am regarded here as an Englishman.[12]

He says he has had fever four times in two months, and at the Falls ("its native country") he had an attack of dysentery which lasted five days. He feels demoralized. "And besides," he adds, "I'm homesick for the sea."

He wanted to hold out and he still hoped to get command of the *Florida,* which was to transport the Katanga expedition directed by Alexandre Delcommune, brother of the acting manager, who no doubt persuaded Alexandre not to give Conrad command of the steamboat.

We have no firsthand evidence as to the cause of his final break with Camille Delcommune, but we have an extremely valuable secondhand item: a letter dated November 29, 1890, from Lublin in Poland, from Madame Marguerite Poradowska to the director of the Société du Haut-Congo in Brussels, paraphrasing several passages from a letter of September 26 which she had just received from Conrad in Kinchassa: [172]

> Moreover, the ship he was to command will not be ready until June, *if then,* and the manager, Mr. Delcommune, has told him frankly that he cannot hope for a promotion or a raise in salary as long as he stays in the Congo. Mr. Delcommune also stated that he is not bound by promises made in Europe unless they are in the contract, and the promises you were good enough to make to him are not in his contract.

After expressing the anxiety felt by Captain Korzeniowski's whole family about the reports of his health, Madame Poradowska informed

12 Letter of September 26, 1890.

the managing director of the company of Conrad's wish to be appointed to the command of one of the ocean-going vessels belonging to one of the trading companies in the Congo that carried on a shuttle service between Banana and Antwerp. If he could be recalled for this purpose, Captain Korzeniowski was quite willing to pay the expenses of his passage home. Madame Poradowska added this significant sentence:

> It is sad to think that a man of Mr. Conrad Korzeniowski's abilities, experienced in the command of ships, should be reduced to this subordinate position and exposed to such noxious diseases.

It is obvious from this letter that the principal cause of Conrad's discontent was Delcommune's refusal to give him command of a ship and his fixed determination to keep him subordinate. Their decision, when Alexandre Delcommune arrived, not to give Conrad command of the *Florida,* was the last straw for him.

By October 19 he had decided to give up everything and go back to Europe with nothing left but the rather vague hope of commanding a sea-going vessel. A few weeks later, just before he reached Europe, Thaddeus Bobrowski wrote to him:

> On the 24th I received your letter of October 19 from Kinchassa informing me of the unhappy ending of your expedition to the Congo and your return to Europe. Madame Marguerite told me of it too, from Lublin, where she heard about it from the director of the Company to whom she had written for news of you.[173]
>
> Although you assure me that the first sea breeze will restore your health, I find your handwriting so changed—no doubt due to the fever and dysentery —that my thoughts since then have not been at all cheerful. I never kept it a secret that I was not in favor of your African venture, but I have been faithful to my principle of letting everyone be happy in his own way.
>
> See a specialist in tropical diseases immediately, for our doctors here know nothing about them and I am not even in a position to tell you to come here for a rest.
>
> Tell me also about the state of your finances, so that I may perhaps help—so far as my circumstances permit.[13]

Captain Korzeniowski had held out as long as he could; he was beaten as much by the effects of the climate as by human malice. His health was seriously impaired. Delcommune's ill will toward Conrad must be regarded as a stroke of luck, for if he had obtained command of the vessel going up the Kasai it is unlikely that Captain Korzeniowski would have come back alive.

We know nothing of the circumstances of his return. He must have left Kinchassa early in November at the latest, since he was at Matadi on December 4. In any case he made the journey from Kin-

[13] Letter of December 27, 1890.

chassa to Léopoldville in a native canoe, as we are told in *A Personal Record:*

... A good many of my other properties ... remained behind through unfortunate accidents of transportation. I call to mind, for instance, a specially awkward turn of the Congo between Kinchassa and Leopoldsville—more particularly when one had to take it at night in a big canoe with only half the proper number of paddlers. I failed in being the second white man on record drowned at that interesting spot through the upsetting of a canoe. The first was a young Belgian officer, but the accident happened some months before my time, and he, too, I believe, was going home; not perhaps quite so ill as myself—but still he was going home. I got round the turn more or less alive, though I was too sick to care whether I did or not, and, always with *Almayer's Folly* amongst my diminishing[174] baggage, I arrived at that delectable capital Boma, where, before the departure of the steamer which was to take me home I had the time to wish myself dead over and over again with perfect sincerity.

The immediate result of this voyage to the Congo was, as Conrad said himself, "a long, long illness and a very dismal convalescence." For the rest of his life his health was to show the permanent effects of this African expedition. He suffered from attacks of fever and gout which made his existence an intermittent martyrdom and his correspondence a long, courageous lament.

On the other hand, we are justified in thinking that this voyage to the Congo and its deplorable consequences played a big part in turning Captain Korzeniowski into the novelist Joseph Conrad.

Edward Garnett . . . told me that Conrad once said to him: "Before the Congo, I was just a mere animal," meaning that for his first fifteen years at sea he had lived almost without being aware of it, carried along by the ardor of his temperament in response to an almost unconscious desire for adventure, without ever thinking about the reasons for his or other people's actions. The illness he contracted in the Congo, by immobilizing him, cutting down his physical activity, and keeping him shut up for long months, forced him to look into himself, to think over the experiences of which his life was so extraordinarily full—though he was still only thirty-three.

It was just before his departure for the Congo that Captain Korzeniowski's literary vocation had begun to take shape. In the baggage he took to Stanley Falls and almost lost on the way back from Kinchassa, was a notebook of a few hundred pages containing the first seven chapters of *Almayer's Folly*. So it is not true that the Congo awoke the latent novelist whom John Conrad Korzeniowski had borne within himself ever since the studious years of his lonely childhood. However, it was the Congo and its consequences that finally shaped his destiny and threw the painful weight of illness into the balance on the side of the novelist, while the seaman was still struggling with him for supremacy.

He was to sail again, but never with the same confidence. From now on he always felt threatened. Despite his unconquerable energy,[175] in the incessant struggle against his old pitiless enemy, the sea, he no longer had that absolute confidence in his own strength that had kept him going so long. A voyage, a victory, as the English saying goes—but he was no longer quite sure of victory.

It is not altogether correct to say, as John Galsworthy does, that "that lingering Congo fever which dogged his health fastened a deep, fitful gloom over his spirit." This gloom was the very basis of his character; he had breathed it since he was born: a gloom not only personal but national: that brave and at the same time desperate attitude of Poland at one of the darkest hours in her history; a gloom intensified by his contact with distant countries, in the solitude of the sea, and revived—horribly—by the sight of colonial greed. If the Congo did not create this deep gloom, it did cause it to spring forth from the very depths of his being, and without any doubt it contributed to those magnificent floods of bitterness which, issuing from the very heart of human darkness, broaden out like a vast river or well up like a cataract to carry to the farthest reaches of its dreams the strength of an unquiet soul and a generous spirit.[176]

ON CONRAD'S USE OF MEMORY*

Edward Garnett

That Conrad's memory had extraordinary wealth of observation to draw on, I had an illuminating proof in *Heart of Darkness*. Some time before he wrote this story of his Congo experience, he narrated it at length one morning while we were walking up and down under a row of Scotch firs that leads down to the Cearne. I listened enthralled while he gave me in detail a very full synopsis of what he intended to write. To my surprise when I saw the printed version I found that about a third of the most striking incidents had been replaced by others of which he had said nothing at all. The effect of the written narrative was no less somber than the spoken, and the end

* From the Introduction to *Letters from Joseph Conrad, 1895-1924*, by Edward Garnett, copyright © 1928, 1956, used by special permission of the publishers, The Bobbs-Merrill Company, Inc. [Title mine. Ed.]

was more consummate; but I regretted the omission of various scenes, one of which described the hero lying sick to death in a native hut, tended by an old negress who brought him water from day to day, when he had been abandoned by all the Belgians. "She saved my life," Conrad said, "the white men never came near me." When on several occasions in those early years I praised his psychological insight he questioned seriously whether he possessed such a power and deplored the lack of opportunities for intimate observation that a sailor's life had offered him. On one occasion, in describing to him a terrible family tragedy of which I had been an eye-witness, Conrad became visibly ill-humored and at last cried out with[14] exasperation, "Nothing of the kind has ever come my way! I have spent half my life knocking about in ships, only getting ashore between voyages. I know nothing, nothing! except from the outside. I have to guess at everything!" This was of course the artist's blind jealousy speaking, coveting the experiences he had not had, and certainly he could have woven a literary masterpiece out of the threads I held, had he ever known the actors.

I may here note that Conrad's "strong foreign accent" in March, 1893, to which Mr. Galsworthy has testified in his *Reminiscences of Joseph Conrad,* seemed to me only slight in November, 1894. But when he read aloud to me some newly written manuscript pages of *An Outcast of the Islands* he mispronounced so many words that I followed him with difficulty. I found then that he had never once heard these English words spoken, but had learned them all from books![15]

INTERPRETING THE STORY

REASSESSMENT OF "HEART OF DARKNESS"*

Douglas Hewitt

One result of this coherence of Conrad's work is that no paraphrase, no dissecting out of a 'subject', is sufficient to convey the intention and significance of his novels and short stories. The themes are not schematic; they are embodied in the imagery, in the structural pattern, in the minute-by-minute flow of the narration. Nevertheless, after the early 'Malayan' phase of *Almayer's Folly, An Outcast of the Islands* and the short stories 'The Lagoon' and 'Karain', he has one recognizable main preoccupation, and it will help to clarify this study if we state it first in general terms, before proceeding to consider individual works in detail. As Conrad himself says in a letter to F. N. Doubleday of 2 June, 1924:

> ... I think that an author who tries to 'explain' is exposing himself to a very great risk—the risk of confessing himself a failure. For a work of art should speak for itself. Yet much could be said on the other side; for it is also clear that a work of art is not a logical demonstration carrying its intention on the face of it.

These books cannot, certainly, be adequately paraphrased; but they can be elucidated and, judging by a good deal of what has been written about them, this elucidation is necessary.

We cannot fail to observe, if we approach Conrad's work without preconceptions, that in almost all his earlier books a penetrating scrutiny is directed against the simple virtues of honesty, courage, pity and fidelity to an unquestioned ideal of conduct. The note is struck as early as *The Nigger of the 'Narcissus'* in the treatment of the sailors' pity for the dying negro, which is seen as 'the latent egoism[16] of tenderness to suffering' which makes them 'highly humanized, tender, complex, excessively decadent'.

In particular we notice the recurrence of one situation which, though it occupies a subordinate place in two or three of the works, dominates many—the situation in which a man who relies on these

* Reprinted with permission of the publisher from Douglas Hewitt, *Conrad: A Reassessment* (Cambridge, England: Bowes & Bowes Publishers Ltd., 1952). [Title mine. Ed.]

simple virtues is confronted by a partially apprehended sense of evil against which they seem powerless. The mere realization of the existence of this evil overwhelms him with a sense of insecurity and casts doubt on the supposedly secure foundations of the ideals themselves; the virtues at last become suspect. Moreover, because of the peculiar structure of Conrad's works, the sharp immediacy of the problems which the confrontation raises and the clear knowledge of the significance to others of the main character's actions combine to prevent these realizations from being disregarded as vague self-questionings or moods which can be ignored. This awareness is often brought about through the recognition by the central character of an obscure link between himself and a manifestation of the evil which he cannot fail to know for what it is.

The 'Malayan' stories deal with treachery and cowardice and with the corruption and disintegration of personality which they cause; the theme is widened and deepened in the succeeding works. The standards by which the traitors are condemned are subjected to scrutiny, and it is the resulting sense of insecurity which makes these books so profoundly disturbing.

Since such generalizations, however, mean little on their own, a detailed study of some of the works is necessary, and 'Heart of Darkness' is one of the best for this purpose; . . . and the title sounds the note of the dominant imagery of this period.

All commentators have pointed out that this story follows very closely the actual events of Conrad's trip to Stanley[17] Falls,[1] but, having noted this, they have generally assumed that it is to be regarded as a picture of the Dark Continent and of Mr Kurtz and that the narrator, Marlow, who plays the part in the book which Conrad played in the actual journey, is merely the more or less transparent medium through which we study the exploitation of the Congo natives and the degradation of Mr Kurtz, the 'hollow man'. In fact, the story is primarily concerned with the effect of the country and of Kurtz on Marlow. This is clear enough from Marlow's own words:

> It was the farthest point of navigation and the culminating point of my experience. It seemed somehow to throw a kind of light on everything about me—and into my thoughts. It was sombre enough, too—and pitiful—not extraordinary in any way—not very clear either. No, not very clear. And yet it seemed to throw a kind of light.[2]

The equation between the farthest point of navigation and the culminating point of Marlow's experience is typical of Conrad's

[1] See "The Congo Diary" in *Last Essays*. The footnotes of Richard Curle emphasize how closely Conrad keeps to autobiography. There is, of course, a certain amount of rearrangement. The exploration party, for instance, arrived in fact *after* Conrad returned from Stanley Falls.

[2] "Heart of Darkness," p. 5.

method. The voyage is both into the impenetrable darkness of Africa and into the darkness of Marlow's thoughts.

Conrad once said to Edward Garnett: 'Before the Congo I was just a mere animal', and the reactions of the originally rather naïve Marlow to his meeting with Kurtz and to the strange country should hold our attention rather than what in 'Geography and Some Explorers' [from the volume *Last Essays*] Conrad describes as: '... the vilest scramble for loot that ever disfigured the history of human conscience and geographical exploration'.

One deviation from autobiography is notable. He changes the facts which would diminish the isolation of Kurtz's settlement on the river. In 'Geography and Some Explorers', describing how he 'smoked a pipe of peace at[18] midnight in the very heart of the African continent, and felt very lonely there', he writes:

> The subdued thundering mutter of the Stanley Falls hung in the heavy night air of the last navigable reach of the Upper Congo, while no more than ten miles away, in Reshid's Camp just above the Falls, the yet unbroken power of the Congo Arabs slumbered uneasily. Their day was over.[3]

In the story, however, Kurtz, is alone 'as though he had been an enchanted princess sleeping in a fabulous castle'.[4]

But though Kurtz's position is isolated, Conrad emphasizes from the first that he is not alone in wickedness. Marlow comes on the scene 'after a lot of Indian Ocean, Pacific, China Seas' and we feel him to represent, in his dealings with the Company, all the forces of straight-forwardness and honesty. He is confronted by incidents which combine the horrible, the wicked and the farcical as he progresses towards the highest point of navigation on the Congo. (For, though Conrad does not give the river a name, he makes it clear enough by his description—and in a noteworthy image:

> It had become a place of darkness. But there was in it one river especially, a mighty big river, that you could see on the map, resembling an immense snake uncoiled, with its head in the sea, its body at rest curving afar over a vast country, and its tail lost in the depths of the land.[5])

The voyage along the African coast has an air of nightmare—of farcical nightmare.

> We pounded along, stopped, landed soldiers; went on, landed custom-house clerks to levy toll in what looked like a God-forsaken wilderness, with a tin shed and a flag-pole lost in it ... we passed various places—trading places—with names like Gran' Bassam, Little Popo; names that seemed to belong to some sordid farce acted in front of a sinister back-cloth.[6]

---

3 *Last Essays*, 1926, p. 25.

4 "Heart of Darkness," p. 37.

5 Ibid., p. 5.

6 Ibid., p. 10.

He turns for relief to the negroes who paddle out in boats from the shore, men who have 'bone, muscle, a wild[19] vitality, an intense energy of movement, that was as natural and true as the surf along their coast'. He strives to keep his grip on the feelings of sanity and normality to which he has been accustomed. 'For a time', he says, 'I would feel I belonged still to a world of straight-forward facts; but the feeling would not last long'.[7]

They come to an anchored warship, shelling the coast, her men dying of disease:

> In the empty immensity of earth, sky, and water, there she was incomprehensible, firing into a continent . . . the general sense of vague and oppressive wonder grew upon me. It was like a weary pilgrimage amongst hints for nightmares.[8]

His wonder and disgust at the 'merry dance of death and trade' grows even stronger on shore. There are manacled negroes, negroes worn out and left to die, pointless blastings of a cliff, pointlessly abandoned stores, and stores that seem never to have been intended for any purpose. It is the inefficiency which revolts Marlow as well as the cruelty and the exploitation of the natives. The nightmare has not yet caught him and he rebels. At the Central Station he asserts his difference from the others:

> 'I went to work the next day' [he says] turning, so to speak, my back on that station. In that way only it seemed to me I could keep my hold on the redeeming facts of life.[9]

He can judge and condemn the 'pilgrims' of trade; he understands their plotting, their hopes that the mysterious Mr Kurtz will be dead before the steamboat can reach him; he watches the flaming hut with common-sense detachment, knowing that there is no hope of saving it and confidently superior to the man with the bucket who hopes to extinguish the conflagration—'I noticed there was a hole in the bottom of his pail'. So far, it is important to realize, he has not succumbed to the nightmare. He retains standards by which he criticizes the traders, and the scope of his criticism[20] is wide. He notes with irony the clean collar of the Company's chief accountant:

> His appearance was certainly that of a hairdresser's dummy; but in the great demoralization of the land he kept up his appearance. That's backbone. His starched collars and got-up shirt-fronts were achievements of character. . . . Thus this man had verily accomplished something. And he was devoted to his books, which were in apple-pie order.[10]

---

[7] Ibid., p. 11.
[8] Ibid., p. 11.
[9] Ibid., p. 19.
[10] Ibid., pp. 14-15.

He refers again to these books:

... the other, bent over his books, was making correct entries of perfectly correct transactions; and fifty feet below the doorstep I could see the still tree-tops of the grove of death.[11]

He looks back in these passages to the description, at the opening of the story, of the Romans colonizing Britain and to the reflections—at the time apparently approving—on the British devotion to efficiency:

What saves us is efficiency—the devotion to efficiency ... The conquest of the earth, which mostly means the taking it away from those who have a different complexion or slightly flatter noses than ourselves, is not a pretty thing when you look into it too much. What redeems it is the idea only. An idea at the back of it; not a sentimental pretence but an idea; and an unselfish belief in the idea ...[12]

Yet he still pins his own faith to a practical task; the redeeming facts to which he chiefly turns are rivets. Against the 'imbecile rapacity' of the pilgrims he sets the job of getting the ship in order: 'Rivets. To get on with the work—to stop the hole'. His immediate work gains for him the significance of a moral principle. The steamboat, he says,

rang under my feet like an empty Huntley & Palmer biscuit-tin kicked along a gutter; she was nothing so solid in make, and rather less pretty in shape, but I had expended enough hard work on her to make me love her ... She had given me a chance to come out a bit—to find out what I could do.[13]

The journey up the river begins to overwhelm him; 'going up that river was like travelling back to the earliest[21] beginnings of the world.' He feels a kinship with the savages who are making an uproar on the banks:

... that was the worst of it [he says]—this suspicion of their not being inhuman. It would come slowly to one ... what thrilled you was just the thought of their humanity—like yours—the thought of your remote kinship with this wild and passionate uproar.[14]

But he does not go ashore 'for a howl and a dance'. He is too busy with practical tasks, with navigating the boat up the treacherous river, seeing that the boiler continues to work, and looking after the native fireman, so that, as he says: 'neither that fireman nor I had time to peer into our creepy thoughts'.

He comes upon another symbol of practical-mindedness and disinterested devotion to duty in the book abandoned by the pile of firewood—*An Inquiry into some Points of Seamanship*.

---

11 Ibid., p. 16.
12 Ibid., p. 4.
13 Ibid., pp. 24-25.
14 Ibid., p. 31.

The simple old sailor, with his talk of chains and purchases, made me forget the jungle and the pilgrims in a delicious sensation of having come upon something unmistakably real.[15]

But 'Towson' is only an interlude—a reminder of Marlow's natural seafaring attitude towards life; the book turns out to be the property of the Russian who has given in to Kurtz with 'a sort of eager fatalism'.

In his meeting with Kurtz, Marlow is finally confronted by the heart of darkness; the earlier manifestations of evil, like his touches of fever, are no more than 'playful paw-strokes of the wilderness, the preliminary trifling before the more serious onslaught'.

The choice of the word 'evil' to describe this seems inevitable. I have used the word so far in this study without apology and without explanation. This is not merely because it is the word which Conrad himself so often uses, but because it corresponds to his entire outlook on moral issues. We can discuss many novelists without using this term, speaking of aberrations of conduct, regrettable failings,[22] weaknesses of character and the like, but the most cursory glance at Conrad's work is enough to convince us that he has a conception of a transcendental evil, embodying itself in individuals—a sense of evil just as great as that of any avowedly Catholic or Calvinist writer.

Against Kurtz Marlow cannot defend himself as he can against the pilgrims and the plottings of the other officials. There is something impressive about the man. Marlow is well aware that

the wilderness had found him out early, and had taken on him a terrible vengeance for the fantastic invasion . . . it had whispered to him things about himself which he did not know, things of which he had no conception till he took counsel with this great solitude—and the whisper had proved irresistibly fascinating. It echoed loudly within him because he was hollow at the core.[16]

Yet he knows that 'he won't be forgotten. Whatever he was, he was not common'.

It is when the manager suggests to Marlow that Kurtz has used an 'unsound method' that we reach one of the most striking and most important phrases of this story—'a choice of nightmares'. We see here that Marlow can no longer defend himself; he can no longer maintain the detachment of a man who relies on standards which are not affected by the corruption and treachery which he meets; he is faced by an experience against which a concern for rivets or for points of seamanship is powerless. He cannot agree, he says, with this formulation of the judgment on Kurtz.

It seemed to me I had never breathed an atmosphere so vile, and I turned mentally to Kurtz for relief—positively for relief. 'Nevertheless I

---

[15] Ibid., p. 33.

[16] Ibid., p. 51.

think Mr Kurtz is a remarkable man', I said with emphasis ... I found myself lumped along with Kurtz as a partisan of methods for which the time was not ripe: I was unsound! Ah! but it was something to have at least a choice of nightmares.[17]

The phrase recurs when Marlow awakes to find that Kurtz has left the boat to rejoin the savages who have worshipped[23] him as a god, and Marlow's bewilderment at the experience is even more clear:

The fact is I was completely unnerved by a sheer blank fright, pure abstract terror, unconnected with any distinct shape of physical danger. What made this emotion so overpowering was—how shall I define it?—the moral shock I received, as if something altogether monstrous, intolerable to thought and odious to the soul, had been thrust upon me unexpectedly ... I left [one of the agents] to his slumbers and leaped ashore. I did not betray Mr Kurtz—it was ordered I should never betray him—it was written I should be loyal to the nightmare of my choice. I was anxious to deal with this shadow by myself alone—and to this day I don't know why I was so jealous of sharing with anyone the peculiar blackness of that experience.[18]

It is useless to ask what is the quality in Kurtz which is absent in the pilgrims. In one sense he is no more than the logical culmination of the hollowness of them all. The difference lies in this—that Marlow can defend himself against the others, he can deny all kinship with them; but just as the manager lumps him along with Kurtz, so he himself feels the link. 'He had kicked himself loose of the earth', Marlow says.

Confound the man! He had kicked the very earth to pieces. He was alone and I before him did not know whether I stood on the ground or floated in the air.[19]

At the very end of the story he reverts in the most explicit terms to this impotence before Kurtz. He speaks of the illusions of the Intended and says:

... that great and saving illusion that shone with an unearthly glow in the darkness, in the triumphant darkness from which I could not have defended her—from which I could not even defend myself.[20]

It is understandable that he should say that his aunt's attempts to nurse up his strength seemed beside the point, because 'it was my imagination that wanted soothing'.

He accepts the bond established between them, just as he has accepted the bond between himself and the savage[24] clamour from

---

17 Ibid., p. 55.
18 Ibid., p. 57.
19 Ibid., p. 59.
20 Ibid., p. 68.

the river bank on the journey upstream. He does not attempt to dissociate himself from the dying man.

> The manager was very placid [he says, describing the return journey] ... The pilgrims looked upon me with disfavour. I was, so to speak, numbered with the dead. It is strange how I accepted this unforeseen partnership, this choice of nightmares forced upon me in the tenebrous land invaded by these mean and greedy phantoms.[21]

Kurtz dies before they reach the down-river station, and then Marlow is ill and thinks that he will die. It is here that we see most explicitly that his simple ideas of virtue, justice and honour prove inadequate to explain to him the nature of the evil which he has seen and the effect which it has had on him.

> However [he says], as you see, I did not go to join Kurtz there and then. I did not. I remained to dream the nightmare out to the end, and to show my loyalty to Kurtz once more. . . . Since I had peeped over the edge myself, I understand better the meaning of his stare, that could not see the flame of the candle, but was wide enough to embrace the whole universe, piercing enough to penetrate all the hearts that beat in the darkness. He had summed up—he had judged. 'The horror!' He was a remarkable man.... And it is not my own extremity I remember best—a vision of greyness without form filled with physical pain, and a careless contempt for the evanescence of all things—even of this pain itself. No! It is his extremity that I seem to have lived through ... It was an affirmation, a moral victory paid for by innumerable defeats, by abominable terrors, by abominable satisfactions. But it was a victory. That is why I have remained loyal to Kurtz to the last. . . .[22] [25]

By the end of the story the darkness which exists in the breast of Kurtz and in the dark continent and in the manager and the pilgrims—the darkness from which Marlow cannot dissociate himself—seems to cover the whole world. The inhabitants of the continental capital seem to him to be foolishly unaware of the omnipresent evil.

> Their bearing, which was simply the bearing of commonplace individuals going about their business in the assurance of perfect safety, was offensive to me like the outrageous flauntings of folly in the face of a danger it was unable to comprehend.[23]

The concluding words, in their imagery, extend the sway of darkness:

> Marlow ceased ... the offing was barred by a black bank of clouds, and the tranquil waterway leading to the uttermost ends of the earth flowed sombre under an overcast sky—seemed to lead into the heart of an immense darkness.[24]

---

21 Ibid., pp. 60-61.
22 Ibid., pp. 62-63.
23 Ibid., p. 63.
24 Ibid., p. 69.

Conrad's mention of how he introduced the word 'silver' into the final paragraph of *Nostromo,* even though he feared that he might spoil it, because the real hero of that book is not the man who gives it its title but the silver itself[25] is enough indication that 'darkness' is here for some more significant reason than merely that of rounding off the story and putting the reader back into the setting of the storytelling Marlow of later years. We are sent back to the beginning of the story, to the words with which Marlow opens: 'And this also has been one of the dark places of the earth'. We know now that it is still one of them, that what Marlow finds in the heart of the African continent is a darkness which every man may be forced to meet within himself. His faith in fidelity and courage is enough to defend him against the pilgrims and their imbecile rapacity, but it is powerless when confronted by the darkness of Mr[26] Kurtz. We can understand why Conrad said: 'Before the Congo I was just a mere animal'.[27]

25 V. Hewitt, *Conrad: A Reassessment,* p. 54, footnote.

THE JOURNEY WITHIN*

Albert J. Guerard

"Heart of Darkness" is the most famous of these personal short novels: a *Pilgrim's Progress* for our pessimistic and psychologizing age. "Before the Congo I was just a mere animal."[1] The living nightmare of 1890 seems to have affected Conrad quite as importantly as did Gide's Congo experience thirty-six years later. The autobiographical basis of the narrative is well known, and its introspective bias obvious; this is Conrad's longest journey into self. But it is[33] well to remember that "Heart of Darkness" is also other if more superficial things: a sensitive and vivid travelogue, and a comment on "the vilest scramble for loot that ever disfigured the history of human conscience and geo-

* Reprinted by permission of the publishers from Albert J. Guerard, *Conrad the Novelist,* Cambridge, Mass.: Harvard University Press, Copyright 1958, by the President and Fellows of Harvard College.

1 Jean-Aubry, *Life and Letters,* I, 141, and *The Sea Dreamer,* p. 175. [p. 100, above.] Reportedly said to Edward Garnett. In his *Joseph Conrad in the Congo* (London, 1926), p. 73. Jean-Aubry gives a slightly different wording: "Before the Congo I was only a simple animal."

graphical exploration."[2] The Congo was much in the public mind in 1889, when Henry Stanley's relief expedition found Emin Pasha (who like Kurtz did not want to be rescued), and it is interesting to note that Conrad was in Brussels during or immediately after Stanley's triumphant welcome there in April 1890.[3] This was just before he set out on his own Congo journey. We do not know how much the Georges Antoine Klein who died on board the *Roi des Belges* resembled the fictional Kurtz, but Stanley himself provided no mean example of a man who could gloss over the extermination of savages with pious moralisms which were very possibly "sincere."

"Heart of Darkness" thus has its important public side, as an angry document on absurd and brutal exploitation. Marlow is treated to the spectacle of a French man-of-war shelling an unseen "enemy" village in the bush, and presently he will wander into the grove at the first company station where the starving and sick Negroes withdraw to die. It is one of the greatest of Conrad's many moments of compassionate rendering. The compassion extends even to the cannibal crew of the *Roi des Belges*. Deprived of the rotten hippo meat they had brought along for food, and paid three nine-inch pieces of brass wire a week, they appear to subsist on "lumps of some stuff like half-cooked dough, of a dirty lavender color" which[34] they keep wrapped in leaves. Conrad here operates through ambiguous suggestion (are the lumps human flesh?) but elsewhere he wants, like Gide after him, to make his complacent European reader *see:* see, for instance, the drunken unkempt official met on the road and three miles farther on the body of the Negro with a bullet hole in his forehead.[4] "Heart of Darkness" is a record of things seen and done. But also Conrad was reacting to the humanitarian pretenses of some of the looters precisely as the novelist today reacts to the moralisms of cold-war propaganda. Then it was ivory that poured from the heart of darkness; now it is

---

[2] *Last Essays,* p. 17. [p. 25 of 1926 issue. Ed.] In "Heart of Darkness" Conrad makes once his usual distinction between British imperialism and the imperialism of other nations. On the map in Brussels there "was a vast amount of red—good to see at any time, because one knows that some real work is done in there." His 1899 letters to E. L. Sanderson and to Mme. Angèle Zagórska on the Boer war express his position clearly. The conspiracy to oust the Briton "is ready to be hatched in other regions. It ... is everlastingly skulking in the Far East. A war there or anywhere but in S. Africa would have been conclusive,—would have been worth the sacrifices" (Jean-Aubry, *Life and Letters,* I, 286). "That they—the Boers—are struggling in good faith for their independence cannot be doubted; but it is also a fact that they have no idea of liberty, which can only be found under the English flag all over the world" (*ibid.,* I, 288).

[3] *Life and Letters,* I, 121, 124; *The Sea Dreamer,* pp. 154-159 [pp. 84-89, above].

[4] Compare "The Congo Diary," [p. 76, above]. Conrad did not use the skeleton tied to a post that he saw on Tuesday, July 29 (*ibid.,* p. 79). It might have seemed too blatant or too "literary" in a novel depending on mortuary imagery from beginning to end.

uranium. Conrad shrewdly recognized—an intuition amply developed in *Nostromo*—that deception is most sinister when it becomes self-deception, and the propagandist takes seriously his own fictions. Kurtz "could get himself to believe anything—anything." The benevolent rhetoric of his seventeen-page report for the International Society for the Suppression of Savage Customs was meant sincerely enough. But a deeper sincerity spoke through his scrawled postscript: "Exterminate all the brutes!" The conservative Conrad (who found Donkin fit to be a labor leader) speaks through the journalist who says that "Kurtz's proper sphere ought to have been politics 'on the popular side.'"

Conrad, again like many novelists today, was both drawn to idealism and repelled by its hypocritical abuse. "The conquest of the earth, which mostly means the taking it away from those who have a different complexion or slightly flatter noses than ourselves, is not a pretty thing when you look into it too much. What redeems it is the idea only. An idea at the back of it; not a sentimental pretence but an idea; and an unselfish belief in the idea . . ." Marlow commits himself to the yet unseen agent partly because Kurtz "had come out equipped with moral ideas of some sort." Anything would seem preferable to the demoralized greed and total cynicism[35] of the others, "the flabby devil" of the Central Station. Later when he discovers what has happened to Kurtz's moral ideas, he remains faithful to the "nightmare of my choice." In *Under Western Eyes* Sophia Antonovna makes a distinction between those who burn and those who rot, and remarks that it is sometimes preferable to burn. The Kurtz who had made himself literally one of the devils of the land, and who in solitude had kicked himself loose of the earth, burns while the others rot. Through violent not flabby evil he exists in the moral universe even before pronouncing judgment on himself with his dying breath. A little too much has been made, I think, of the redemptive value of those two words—"The horror!" But none of the company "pilgrims" could have uttered them.

The redemptive view is Catholic, of course, though no priest was in attendance; Kurtz can repent as the gunman of *The Power and the Glory* cannot. "Heart of Darkness" (still at this public and wholly conscious level) combines a Victorian ethic and late Victorian fear of the white man's deterioration with a distinctly Catholic psychology. We are protected from ourselves by society with its laws and its watchful neighbors, Marlow observes. And we are protected by work. "You wonder I didn't go ashore for a howl and a dance? Well, no—I didn't. Fine sentiments, you say? Fine sentiments, be hanged! I had no time. I had to mess about with white-lead and strips of woolen blanket helping to put bandages on those leaky steam-pipes." But when the external restraints of society and work are removed, we must meet the challenge and temptation of savage reversion with our "own inborn strength. Principles won't do." This inborn strength appears to include restraint—the restraint that Kurtz lacked and the cannibal crew of the *Roi des Belges* surprisingly possessed. The hollow man, whose evil is the evil of *vacancy,* succumbs. And in their different degrees the pilgrims and Kurtz share this hollowness. "Perhaps there was nothing within" the manager of the Central Station. "Such a suspicion made one pause—for out there there were no external checks." And there was nothing inside the brickmaker,[36] that papier-maché Mephistopheles, "but a little loose dirt, maybe."

As for Kurtz, the wilderness "echoed loudly within him because he was hollow at the core." Perhaps the chief contradiction of "Heart of Darkness" is that it suggests and dramatizes evil as an active energy (Kurtz and his unspeakable lusts) but defines evil as vacancy. The primitive (and here the contradiction is only verbal) is compact of passion and apathy. "I was struck by the fire of his eyes and the composed languor of his expression ... This shadow looked satiated and calm, as though for the moment it had had its fill of all the emotions." Of the two menaces—the unspeakable desires and the apathy—apathy surely seemed the greater to Conrad. Hence we cannot quite believe the response of Marlow's heart to the beating of the tom-toms. This is, I think, the story's minor but central flaw, and the source of an unfruitful ambiguity: that it slightly overdoes the kinship with the "passionate uproar," slightly undervalues the temptation of inertia.

In any event, it is time to recognize that the story is not primarily about Kurtz or about the brutality of Belgian officials but about Marlow its narrator. To what extent it also expresses the Joseph Conrad a biographer might conceivably recover, who in 1898 still felt a debt must be paid for his Congo journey and who paid it by the writing of this story, is doubtless an insoluble question. I suspect two facts (of a possible several hundred) are important. First, that going to the Congo was the enactment of a childhood wish associated with the disapproved childhood ambition to go to sea, and that this belated enactment was itself profoundly disapproved, in 1890, by the uncle and guardian.[5] It was another gesture of a man bent on throwing his life away. But even more important may be the guilt of complicity, just such a guilt as many novelists of the Second World War have been obliged to work off. What Conrad thought of the expedition of the Katanga Company of 1890-1892 is accurately reflected in his remarks on the "Eldorado Exploring Expedition" of "Heart of Darkness": "It was reckless without hardihood, greedy[37] without audacity, and cruel without courage ... with no more moral purpose at the back of it than there is in burglars breaking into a safe." Yet Conrad hoped to obtain command of the expedition's ship even after he had returned from the initiatory voyage dramatized in his novel. Thus the adventurous Conrad and

[5] *Life and Letters,* I, 137; *The Sea Dreamer,* p. 171 [p. 97, above].

Conrad the moralist may have experienced collision. But the collision, again as with so many novelists of the second war, could well have been deferred and retrospective, not felt intensely at the time.

So much for the elusive Conrad of the biographers and of the "Congo Diary." Substantially and in its central emphasis "Heart of Darkness" concerns Marlow (projection to whatever great or small degree of a more irrecoverable Conrad) and his journey toward and through certain facets or potentialities of self. F. R. Leavis seems to regard him as a narrator only, providing a "specific and concretely realized point of view."[6] But Marlow reiterates often enough that he is recounting a spiritual voyage of self-discovery. He remarks casually but crucially that he did not know himself before setting out, and that he likes work for the chance it provides to "find yourself ... what no other man can ever know." The Inner Station "was the farthest point of navigation and the culminating point of my experience." At a material and rather superficial level, the journey is through the temptation of atavism. It is a record of "remote kinship" with the "wild and passionate uproar," of a "trace of a response" to it, of a final rejection of the "fascination of the abomination." And why should there not be the trace of a response? "The mind of man is capable of anything—because everything is in it, all the past as well as all the future." Marlow's temptation is made concrete through his exposure to Kurtz, a white man and sometime idealist who had fully responded to the wilderness: a potential and fallen self. "I had turned to the wilderness really, not to Mr. Kurtz." At the climax Marlow follows Kurtz ashore, confounds the beat of the drum with the beating of his heart, goes through the ordeal of looking into Kurtz's "mad soul," and brings him back to the ship. He returns to Europe a changed and more knowing man. Ordinary[38] people are now "intruders whose knowledge of life was to me an irritating pretence, because I felt so sure they could not possibly know the things I knew."

On this literal plane, and when the events are so abstracted from the dream-sensation conveying them, it is hard to take Marlow's plight very seriously. Will he, the busy captain and moralizing narrator, also revert to savagery, go ashore for a howl and a dance, indulge unspeakable lusts? The late Victorian reader (and possibly Conrad himself) could take this more seriously than we; could literally believe not merely in a Kurtz's deterioration through months of solitude but also in the sudden reversions to the "beast" of naturalistic fiction. Insofar as Conrad does want us to take it seriously and literally, we must admit the nominal triumph of a currently accepted but false psychology over his own truer intuitions. But the triumph is only nominal. For the personal narrative is unmistakably authentic, which means that it

[6] F. R. Leavis, *The Great Tradition* (London, 1948), p. 183.

explores something truer, more fundamental, and distinctly less material; the night journey into the unconscious, and confrontation of an entity within the self. "I flung one shoe overboard, and became aware that that was exactly what I had been looking forward to—a talk with Kurtz." It little matters what, in terms of psychological symbolism, we call this double or say he represents: whether the Freudian id or the Jungian shadow or more vaguely the outlaw. And I am afraid it is impossible to say where Conrad's conscious understanding of his story began and ended. The important thing is that the introspective plunge and powerful dream seem true; and are therefore inevitably moving.

Certain circumstances of Marlow's voyage, looked at in these terms, take on a new importance. The true night journey can occur (except during analysis) only in sleep or in the waking dream of a profoundly intuitive mind. Marlow insists more than is necessary on the dreamlike quality of his narrative. "It seems to me I am trying to tell you a dream—making a vain attempt, because no relation of a dream can convey the dream-sensation, that commingling of absurdity, surprise, and bewilderment in a tremor of struggling revolt . . ."[39] Even before leaving Brussels Marlow felt as though he "were about to set off for the center of the earth," not the center of a continent.[7] The introspective voyager leaves his familiar rational world, is "cut off from the comprehension" of his surroundings; his steamer toils "along slowly on the edge of a black and incomprehensible frenzy." As the crisis approaches, the dreamer and his ship move through a silence that "seemed unnatural, like a state of trance"; then enter (a few miles below the Inner Station) a deep fog. "The approach to this Kurtz grubbing for ivory in the wretched bush was beset by as many dangers as though he had been an enchanted princess sleeping in a fabulous castle."[8] Later, Marlow's task is to try "to break the spell" of the wilderness that holds Kurtz entranced.

The approach to the unconscious and primitive may be aided by a savage or half-savage guide, and may require the token removal of civilized trappings or aids; both conceptions are beautifully dramatized in Faulkner's "The Bear." In "Heart of Darkness" the token "relinquishment" and the death of the half-savage guide are connected. The helmsman falling at Marlow's feet casts blood on his shoes, which he

---

[7] Lilian Feder finds a number of parallels with the sixth book of the *Aeneid* in "Marlow's Descent into Hell," *Nineteenth-Century Fiction,* IX (March 1955) 280-292; Robert O. Evans finds chiefly the influence of Dante's *Inferno* in "Conrad's Underworld," *Modern Fiction Studies,* II (May 1956), 56-62 [and pp. 137-145, below]. My views on literary influence differ from those of Miss Feder and Mr. Evans. But echoes and overtones may exist. We may apply to "Heart of Darkness" Thomas Mann's words on *Death in Venice:* a little work of "inexhaustible allusiveness."

[8] The analogy of unspeakable Kurtz and enchanted princess may well be an intended irony. But there may be some significance in the fact that this once the double is imagined as an entranced feminine figure.

is "morbidly anxious" to change and in fact throws overboard.[9] (The rescue of Wait in *The Nigger of the "Narcissus"* shows a similar pattern.) Here we have presumably entered an area of unconscious creation; the dream is true but the teller may have no idea why it is. So too, possibly, a psychic need as well as literary tact compelled Conrad to defer the meeting between Marlow and Kurtz for some three thousand words after announcing that it took place. We think we are about to meet Kurtz at last. But instead Marlow leaps ahead to his meeting with the "Intended"; comments on Kurtz's megalomania[40] and assumption of his place among the devils of the land; reports on the seventeen-page pamphlet; relates his meeting and conversation with Kurtz's harlequin disciple—and only then tells of seeing through his binoculars the heads on the stakes surrounding Kurtz's house. This is the "evasive" Conrad in full play, deferring what we most want to know and see; perhaps compelled to defer climax in this way. The tactic is dramatically effective, though possibly carried to excess: we are told on the authority of completed knowledge certain things we would have found hard to believe had they been presented through a slow consecutive realistic discovery. But also it can be argued that it was psychologically impossible for Marlow to go at once to Kurtz's house with the others. The double must be brought on board the ship, and the first confrontation must occur there. We are reminded of Leggatt in the narrator's cabin, of the trapped Wait on the *Narcissus.* The incorporation and alliance between the two becomes material, and the identification of "selves."

Hence the shock Marlow experiences when he discovers that Kurtz's cabin is empty and his secret sharer gone; a part of himself has vanished. "What made this emotion so overpowering was—how shall I define it?—the moral shock I received, as if something altogether monstrous, intolerable to thought and odious to the soul, had been thrust upon me unexpectedly." And now he must risk the ultimate confrontation in a true solitude and must do so on shore. "I was anxious to deal with this shadow by myself alone—and to this day I don't know why I was so jealous of sharing with anyone the peculiar blackness of that experience." He follows the crawling Kurtz through the grass; comes upon him "long, pale, indistinct, like a vapor exhaled by the earth." ("I had cut him off cleverly . . .") We are told very little of what Kurtz said in the moments that follow; and little of his incoherent discourses after he is brought back to the ship. "His was an impenetrable darkness. I looked at him as you peer down at a man who

[9] Like any obscure human act, this one invites several interpretations, beginning with the simple washing away of guilt. The fear of the blood may be, however, a fear of the primitive toward which Marlow is moving. To throw the shoes overboard would then mean a token rejection of the savage, not the civilized-rational. In any event it seems plausible to have blood at this stage of a true initiation story.

is lying at the bottom of a precipice where the sun never shines"—a comment less vague and rhetorical, in terms of psychic geography, than it may seem at a first[41] reading. And then Kurtz is dead, taken off the ship, his body buried in a "muddy hole." With the confrontation over, Marlow must still emerge from environing darkness, and does so through that other deep fog of sickness. The identification is not yet completely broken. "And it is not my own extremity I remember best—a vision of grayness without form filled with physical pain, and a careless contempt for the evanescence of all things—even of this pain itself. No! It is his extremity that I seem to have lived through." Only in the atonement of his lie to Kurtz's "Intended," back in the sepulchral city, does the experience come truly to an end. "I laid the ghost of his gifts at last with a lie . . ."

Such seems to be the content of the dream. If my summary has even a partial validity it should explain and to an extent justify some of the "adjectival and worse than supererogatory insistence" to which F. R. Leavis (who sees only the travelogue and the portrait of Kurtz) objects. I am willing to grant that the unspeakable rites and unspeakable secrets become wearisome, but the fact—at once literary and psychological—is that they must remain *unspoken*. A confrontation with such a double and facet of the unconscious cannot be reported through realistic dialogue; the conversations must remain as shadowy as the narrator's conversations with Leggatt. So too when Marlow finds it hard to define the moral shock he received on seeing the empty cabin, or when he says he doesn't know why he was jealous of sharing his experience, I think we can take him literally . . . and in a sense even be thankful for his uncertainty. The greater tautness and economy of "The Secret Sharer" comes from its larger conscious awareness of the psychological process it describes; from its more deliberate use of the double as symbol. And of the two stories I happen to prefer it. But it may be the groping, fumbling "Heart of Darkness" takes us into a deeper region of the mind. If the story is not about this deeper region, and not about Marlow himself, its length is quite indefensible. But even if one were to allow that the final section is about Kurtz (which I think simply absurd), a vivid pictorial record of his unspeakable lusts and gratifications[42] would surely have been ludicrous. I share Mr. Leavis' admiration for the heads on the stakes. But not even Kurtz could have supported many such particulars.[10] [43]

---

[10] The reader irritated by the hallucinated atmosphere and subjective preoccupation of "Heart of Darkness" should turn to Robert Louis Stevenson's short novel, *The Beach of Falesá* (1892). A new trader, Wiltshire, takes a native mistress, and finds himself—thanks to a rival trader (Case)—virtually excommunicated. The situation distantly resembles that of Willems in *The Outcast of the Islands*. Later, Wiltshire goes inland to discover the source of Case's power over the natives; he has heard stories that his rival worships or traffics with devils. He finds an Æolian harp in a tree (to simulate ghostly voices) and presently the place of worship:

"Along all the top of it was a line of queer figures, idols or scarecrows, or what not. They had carved and painted faces, ugly to view, their eyes and teeth were of shell, their hair and their bright clothes blew in the wind, and some of them worked with the tugging ...

"Then it came in my mind that Case had let out to me the first day that he was a good forger of island curiosities, a thing by which so many traders turn an honest penny. And with that I saw the whole business, and how this display served the man a double purpose: first of all, to season his curiosities and then to frighten those that came to visit him."

Had Conrad read *The Beach of Falesá* before writing "Heart of Darkness"? The question is unimportant. The important thing is to recognize the immense distance from Case's carved faces to the skulls on Kurtz's palisade; from Case's pretended traffic with devils to Kurtz's role as one of the devils of the land; from Wiltshire's canny outwitting of a rival trader to Marlow's dark inward journey; from the inert jungle of Stevenson's South Pacific to the charged symbolic jungle of Conrad's Congo. The nighttime meeting of Case and Wiltshire is merely an exciting physical struggle. *The Beach of Falesá* is a good manly yarn totally bereft of psychological intuition.

THE DUTY OF MARLOW

MARLOW'S FUNCTION*

M. C. Bradbrook

Marlow's function is to comment. Although a complete character and not a puppet, he shares Conrad's fundamental outlook, and so can speak for him. Comment is necessary since Conrad could not draw a character from the inside; he could not dramatise another man's mind—as for example Browning dramatises all the characters of *The Ring and the Book,* Henry James the characters of *The Awkward Age,* or E. M. Forster some of the characters of *A Passage to India.* That this was a genuine incapacity and not a wanton self-limitation on Conrad's part is proved by the failure of Almayer and—even more disastrous—of Harvey in *The Return.* "He could not invent. He could not see things which were not, or never had been, before his eyes. His whole magnificent perceptiveness depended absolutely on the senses" (*Joseph Conrad,* p. 118).[1] Hence Conrad's reliance on his "contacts". Given the smallest core[21] of fact, he could penetrate, illuminate, fix its significance. In *Nostromo* he moved a Mediterranean sailor to the coast of South America and in *The Rover* and *Suspense* he puts the same man into the Napoleonic period: but he could neither invent a wholly fantastic character, like Dickens's Mr Pickwick, or present a character from within, like Mr Joyce's Stephen Dedalus. "He can look into the depths of another man's mind. His astounding power of physical vision enabled him to tell a character from its external manifestations".[2] He could read the weather signs of a man's face. But he could do no more than put the weather signs down, so selected that his reader could see them too. Unless he were to compromise the integrity of the story with a "dear reader" in Thackeray's manner, he could not even give the sign post, the directing line of enunciation

*Reprinted with permission of the publisher from M. C. Bradbrook, *Joseph Conrad: Poland's English Genius* (Cambridge, England: Cambridge University Press, 1942). [Title mine. Ed.]

1 Confirmed by Conrad: "As for the story itself it is true enough in its essentials. The sustained invention of a really telling lie demands a talent which I do not possess." (*Tales of Unrest:* Author's Note, p. vii.)

2 Edward Crankshaw, *Joseph Conrad, Some aspects of the art of the novel* (John Lane, The Bodley Head, 1936).

which any complex novel must use at times. The solution was Marlow, a character whose view is not more authoritative, more of an "Idea" or a "Fact"[3] than the rest of the book, yet whose comment steadies the work in illumination of "the truth, manifold and one, underlying its every aspect". . . .[22]

[In *The Heart of Darkness* Conrad achieves a "sombre theme (which) had to be given a sinister resonance, a tonality of its own. . . ."] In this sinister resonance *The Heart of Darkness* is supreme; and it is maintained almost wholly in terms of the scene. It opens in the dusky Thames estuary where Marlow is thinking "And this also has been one of the dark places of the earth" (p. 3)—in the days when the Romans landed. Then come his reminiscences of the Congo trip, of the tropical brilliance of sunshine surrounding the dying and exploited Negroes, the dying and utterly perverted Kurtz, equally exploited in his way, now the god of a savage tribe, and enslaved by the primitive and abominable lusts that burgeon from his mind in the fecund jungle mud. . . .[28] The atmosphere of the grave was not stronger in the jungle itself. And here is the girl, [Kurtz's fiancée]:

> All the sad light of the cloudy evening had taken refuge on her forehead. The fair hair, the pale visage, the pure brow seemed surrounded by an ashy halo from which the dark eyes looked out at me. (p. 66)

This removed, spiritual creature cherishes an angelic illusion of the beauty of Kurtz's character, which brings back to Marlow all the more vividly the end of that lost soul: and, acutely haunted by Kurtz's last words "The horror! The horror!" so that they seem to ring in the twilit rooms, he lies the hero into a beautiful ending.

> I could not tell her. It would have been too dark—too dark altogether. (p. 69)

And then the whole episode is at once distanced and commented upon by the closing paragraph—a look downstream on the darkling Thames. It is a resolution of the tragic theme which is at once simpler and more subtle than that involving the simplest human feelings: an effect akin to the line in Webster's *Duchess of Malfi,* "Look you, the stars shine still",[29] or that which introduces the death scene of Shakespeare's Antony: "Sometimes we see a cloud that's dragonish."

> "We have lost the first of the ebb", said the Director suddenly. I raised my head. The offing was barred by a black bank of clouds, and the tranquil waterway leading to the uttermost ends of the earth flowed sombre under an overcast sky—seemed to lead into the heart of an immense darkness. (p. 69)

[3] "The thinker plunges into ideas, the scientist into facts. . . . It is otherwise with the artist." (*The Nigger of the Narcissus,* Author's Preface, p. vii.)

The story carries this particular method of suggestion to its limits. It is most delicately counterpoised between what is seen and what is sensed or perceived, by means of similes which transform Conrad's powers of description into powers of analysis and creation. With no departure from the descriptive method, every incident yet deepens the force of the truth manifold and one which pervades the tale. There are contrasts and echoes: Marlow's aunt, for instance, in her illusion that he will be an apostle of progress in Darkest Africa provokes ironic reflections from her nephew on the feminine powers of self-deception, which would be wrong at the poignant interview with the fiancée of Kurtz, but which reverberate there with a "sinister resonance". Again the queer knitting women who inhabit the office in Belgium from which this chain of exploitation starts reoccur to Marlow at one of his worst moments as queer things to be at the other end of this affair—and they become shadowy Fates or at least *tricoteuses* in recollection. The complexity is a living complexity;[30] and Conrad's renunciation of the supernatural gives it all the close texture of actual life. There are no occult powers among the natives, Kurtz's adorers, who are just spied at their savage rites; in the day, they are pitiful creatures frightened off by the screech of the steamer's whistle. They are even more pitiful than the starved and dying negroes of the coast or the ship's crew who are paid with brass wire but given no food, so that when the steersman is killed Marlow has to throw him overboard at once before his carcase rouses the appetite of his fellows. Yet all these figures only deepen in garish splendour the death of Kurtz—the trappings of corruption. . . .[31]

APOLOGY FOR MARLOW*

W. Y. Tindall

The trouble with Conrad, indeed, the only trouble, says F. R. Leavis, is Marlow. "Heart of Darkness," found good by some good critics, is so generally "marred" by Marlow's adjectives that it sinks into place beside *Lord Jim* among minor works. In "Youth," a "cheap

* In R. C. Rathburn and M. Steinmann, Jr., eds., *From Jane Austen to Joseph Conrad* (Minneapolis: University of Minnesota Press, 1959). Reprinted by permission of the author.

insistence" on glamor makes Conrad seem a Kipling of the South Seas, if not worse. It may be that in *Chance* Conrad-Marlow rises above such "shockingly bad magazine stuff" to a kind of technical respectability, but, save for that, stories in which Marlow figures cannot be counted among the major works: *Nostromo, Under Western Eyes, The Secret Agent,* and some others in a hierarchy of values, unsupported but proclaimed. Abandoning the "objective correlative" when Marlow is around, Leavis continues, Conrad becomes "intent on making a virtue out of not knowing what he means. The vague and unrealizable, he asserts with a strained impressiveness, is the profoundly and tremendously significant." The trouble with Leavis seems failure to read the text or else to understand it.

It is good to sit down with familiar things again. (I owe a general debt to my seminar in Conrad, Spring, 1957.) Sitting there, let us look again at Marlow to find if years have brought us wisdom or new light. Let Leavis be occasion, not our theme.

Our scrutiny may discover the intention of those works in which Marlow is an element, not the intention of that fallacy at Yale but embodied intention, there in the text and not to be separated from what is often called idea or theme, the intention that elements must serve and critics fix. With the text before us, we may discover or at least accost some values of Marlow as a functioning element and of his stories as organizations of elements. Such matters are puzzling; for when Marlow is there, little is plain. In love with "enigma," he tells "inscrutable" stories.

Other critics besides Leavis have confused Marlow with his creator. When Marlow speaks they think it Conrad; and one must admit some[274] reason for this confusion. As Conrad's other writings prove, Marlow shares some of Conrad's ideas, his moral concerns, and his delight in irony. It requires little critical awareness, however, to discover that Marlow, in spite of monocle and beard (if, indeed, he wears them), is a creature distinct from his creator. Conrad, who appears at the beginning and end and sometimes in the middle of the Marlow books, listens to Marlow and tells us what he tells him. To Conrad, Marlow is the object as Jim or Kurtz seems Marlow's. Marlow may owe something to Conrad's desire for a mask in Yeats's sense of the word, but a mask is a device for achieving impersonality, drama, and distance. No longer subject but object, Marlow has been distanced to the point where Conrad can regard him as another and use him not with the warm concern we devote to ourselves but with aesthetic detachment as an artist should. Marlow is matter to be handled and shaped. Maybe his closest parallel is Stephen Dedalus, who, although resembling his creator in many ways, is nonetheless someone else. Like Stephen, Marlow often exposes his imperfections to the mocking eye.

As Marlow serves the interests of aesthetic distance, so he serves those of realism. Like the impressionists and those who were to employ the stream of consciousness, Conrad seems to have been persuaded for a time that reality, consisting of mental refractions, is subjective. Reality in a Marlow story is in Marlow's head, not somewhere else. Moreover, the "illusion of life" that Conrad admires in the Preface to *The Nigger of the Narcissus* may be improved by a witness's report. Recounted by one who was there or, if not, by one who has received reports from those who were, the story carries a greater air of verisimilitude than an omniscient narrator commands. That, at least, is the theory. Marlow's almost incredible long-windedness might appear to injure this necessary illusion; but as Conrad assures us in the Preface to *Lord Jim,* the length of Marlow's monologue is not so great as it seems, and even if it were, might be excused by cigars, drink, and company. Preface and text alike may persuade us that Marlow was designed for suspending disbelief and establishing verisimilitude. Since, however, these depend upon no particular device or method but upon the success of any, this aspect of Marlow is not central. Marlow as center of reality is.

Conrad seems during this time to have approximated Henry James's ideas of reality. For that reason many critics have traced Marlow's origin to the master, who invented his observer several years before the emergence[275] of Marlow. Seeing him as a development of the Jamesian observer, they have found him a kind of bearded Maisie or a monocled anticipation of Strether. Of their family maybe, Marlow differs nevertheless in so many particulars from his assumed prototype and successor that it is likely he owes Maisie no more than a possible hint. James, looking into the head of his observer, presents a selection of what goes on there. His role is that of interpreter, Conrad's of reporter. Maisie receives impressions which James attends to; Marlow, an amateur philosopher, a compulsive talker, and a kind of artist, considers, colors, and shapes his impressions by himself, while Conrad, aloof, scribbles in his notebook. Maisie's experience is immediate and current, whereas Marlow's, dependent upon memory where it receives further refraction, is distant in time and place. These differences make it clear that if, indifferent to fallacies, we allow genesis, we should look elsewhere for Marlow's.

I think that the idea of Marlow can be traced back to the inner demands of Conrad's work, immediately to *The Nigger of the Narcissus,* of which the Marlow stories seem natural developments—in several ways; but let us limit ourselves for the moment to what Percy Lubbock calls point of view. Since Marlow among other things is an embodied point of view, that limitation is suitable. The story of James Wait and the ship *Narcissus* is told by someone who, like the narrator of the Cyclops episode of *Ulysses,* is nameless and apparently disembodied. No more than a voice, this ghostly attendant employs first person nevertheless: "we" and finally "I." In spite of this long personal ascent from plural to singular, he seems not altogether there. Of and yet apart from the crew whose solidarity is his main concern, he speaks to none, avoids all action, and fails to limit his observations to what is possible. He is present at the interviews of Donkin and Wait and of Wait and the cook although these interviews are without third parties. With equal ease he enters the first mate's head (or else that of the second) to tell us what goes on. He gets around—and as he gets there he anticipates Marlow now and again in his devotion to simile, his moral anxiety, his delight in "enigma," and his surrender to "the fascination of the incomprehensible." It is plain that this concerned yet ghostly voice is an experiment, an unsuccessful experiment perhaps, marking a transition between omniscience and a personified observer. Marlow, developing from this voice, improves it. Equipped with personality, character, limits, attitude, and tone—in a word, with body—Charlie Marlow and his conspiring voice become authentic. More than[276] observant, he not only plays his part in the action but subsumes it, leaving that ancestral voice neither here nor there.

Not Conrad's occasional description, then, but this voice determines Marlow, who, far from Polish, emerges as the Victorian gentleman, the embodiment maybe of Conrad's aspiration. Almost a Colonel Blimp at times, Marlow nevertheless exceeds that caricature in sensibility and complexity. The stiff upper lip conceals the man of feeling and the civilized European. His monocle (if any) might be taken as his image; for rays of light through a single lens are both bent and (if we may pass from the physical to the social sense of this metaphor) distanced. Conrad's monocle, proved by photography, is not, as the wit put it in another connection, a monocle built for two; for Marlow's is singular in every sense. Monocular vision implies ideas, biases, principles, even obsessions. Marlow's are plainly there, changing things. In love with conscious order and light, he detests disorder and darkness. Devoted to duty, fidelity, and prudence as a navigator and master must be, he observes in "Heart of Darkness," at a moment of savage and commercial confusion: "I looked ahead—piloting." As he proceeds, he ruminates in the manner of the popular philosopher on the nature of things. Their nature, we discover, is not altogether different from that observed by Hardy or, indeed, by Conrad—if we may trust his letters. Marlow shares with his creator the all but existentialist conviction that however meaningless and hopeless things are, we must cherish ideals and by their aid change necessary defeat to a kind of futile victory. Such human victories, general defeats, and all things else are mixed and dubious. For this reason too Marlow is obsessed with enigmas and uncertainties. They are part of the nature of things. We can never be sure in this uncertain place, but we must try.

As for attitude: at once cynical and sentimental, Marlow is given to pity and impatience. Maybe his term "romantic" describes him best. Although he fails to define it, this term, as he uses it, seems to include imagination, illusion, anxiety, and concern with self. Marlow has little humor, though he laughs once or twice, as, for example, when Fyne falls down a hole in the dark. If little humor and less wit, there is plenty of irony; and that provides his common tone. Like many ironists, Marlow is committed, *engagé*. All this is apparent enough; but Marlow, changing with the years, reveals new aspects in each story from "Youth" to *Chance*. Whether early, middle, or late, however, and whatever his apparent commitments, Marlow has Marlow in mind.[277]

In "Youth" we have Marlow on Marlow, a congenial theme for this worrier. Here alone among his monologues, subject is plainly one with object and the apparent with the actual. Before an audience composed of Conrad and a variety of bankers, brokers, and directors, Marlow, undescribed but more or less mature, ruminates about himself when young and foolish. As memory searches the past, bringing it to present light, two times, providing tension, center our interest and his own. Marlow's times, simpler than those of Proust's Marcel, may remind us of Eliot's pastness of the past and its presence; for Marlow finds irony in their coincidence—not irony alone, however, but nostalgia and sentiment as well. Most suitably defined at his debut as a sentimental ironist, Marlow makes a point of what he calls "the romance of illusions" and the pleasing folly of "the good old time." His far from tranquil recollections are suitably punctuated. "O youth!" he exclaims, "The strength of it, the faith of it, the imagination of it! . . . Oh, the glamour of youth!" These periodic exclamations compose what Leavis calls Conrad's "cheap insistence" on glamor; but a moment's scrutiny shows that Marlow is speaking, that he is the kind of man who, unwilling to let a thing reveal itself, insists on underlining it. An amateur as yet at telling tales and otherwise imperfect, Marlow is allowed by Conrad to expose himself—in a kind of double exposure. While old Marlow exposes young Marlow to sentimental irony, ironic Conrad, aloof, silent, and listening among men of affairs, lets innocent old Marlow show old Marlow up. The anxious awkwardness and sentimentality that he displays are important; for the nature of Marlow is the theme. What escapes Leavis, detained by an element, is the total structure with its tone, feeling, sense, and intention. We too may dislike Marlow and his manner or method, but we must not blame Conrad for a dramatic revelation of middle-aged nostalgia or the discursive insistency that seems its accomplice. Those thematic exclamations and asides, inseparable from the portrait of Marlow, are the thing itself.

Searching possibilities of Marlow as subject and object, Conrad followed this simple tale with one of greater density or specific gravity, which may be signs or at least metaphors of value. A tale at once complex and ambiguous, "Heart of Darkness" is ostensibly the story of Marlow's quest for Kurtz. Actually Marlow is questing for himself: "The most you can hope," he says, "is some knowledge of yourself." While seeking assurance and knowledge, he exposes himself once more to Conrad's distant eye. But Marlow has developed. Not only a discursive commentator, he has[278] become an imagist as well; and developing in other directions, he has acquired moral concerns. That love of mystery which appears now and again in "Youth," emerges here as one of Marlow's obsessions.

"Image" and "symbol," terms used by Marlow, indicate his new method of presentation—at least in part. By "image," a term he applies to Kurtz and the wild woman, he seems to mean a significant but more or less limited concretion; and by "symbol," a term he applies to skulls on posts, he seems to mean a less definite, more generally suggestive concretion. Rusting machinery in the Belgian wasteland and the gunboat shelling the forest are images in his sense; whereas the enigmatic forest is a symbol. As if familiar with the Preface to *The Nigger of the Narcissus,* Marlow sometimes presents his vision in plastic, sensuous forms that seem designed to "reveal" or "disclose" embodied meaning to an audience that must take these offerings as it can. Conrad's Preface, a symbolist manifesto, is not unlike Yeats's contemporary essay "The Symbolism of Poetry." We have no assurance that Marlow has read Conrad or Yeats on symbolism, but as he tells us in "Youth," he has read Carlyle's *Sartor Resartus* with its famous chapter on symbol, and it seems likely from the text that he knows Baudelaire—as Conrad did. In "Heart of Darkness" Marlow's childish interest in the "delightful mystery" of maps and his consequent journey to the "unknown" suggest Baudelaire's "Le Voyage" as Marlow's dandy at the trading post suggests Baudelaire's ideal man. Comparing his forest to a "temple," Marlow calls to mind the forest of Baudelaire's "Correspondences," which also allows obscure, confusing intimations to emerge.

In the prelude to "Heart of Darkness" Conrad tells us that for Marlow "the meaning of an episode was not inside it like a kernel but outside, enveloping the tale which brought it out only as a glow brings out a haze." This "misty halo" (not unlike the white fog encountered on the Congo) seems to have little in common with the inner truth, lying deep below the surface, that Marlow seeks; but only a difference of metaphor separates these attempts to fix the meaning of symbol. Wherever its meaning lies—whether in halo, fog, or kernel—Marlow's principal symbol, aside from the forest, is the voyage, that, he says in "Youth," seems "ordered for the illustration of life, that might stand for a symbol of existence." His trip up the Congo "seemed to throw a kind of light on everything about me—and into my thoughts." Not "very clear," to be sure, "yet it seemed to throw a kind of light." That Marlow saw his outer adventure as the archetypal embodiment of an inner adventure is clear.[279]

Like Baudelaire, Marlow is seldom content to let his concretions alone. Sometimes he tries to explain them and almost always, driven by anxiety, he anticipates our reaction by stating his own. Marlow, after all, is not early T. S. Eliot. Adjectives and similes, not unlike the eager nouns by which the captain of "The Secret Sharer" tries to fix his delusion, are Marlow's attempts to give his response to halo or kernel and to fix his impression of the images he picks as subjective correlatives. He finds the women knitting black wool "fateful," and the "expressive and puzzling" skulls indicative of moral deficiency. Even the forest is restricted by Marlow's guesses to our primitive, repressed, and hidden desires, below "permitted aspirations." Such discursive limitations, however, are legitimate in this context; for the story is not about knitting women, forests, or even Kurtz, but about Marlow's response to them.

Trying to explain his dark forest, Marlow commonly finds it enigmatic, its darkness properly shrouded in white fog. In this respect Marlow resembles the crew of the *Narcissus,* who, like critics confronted by a text, find Wait, another dark thing, ambiguous. Far from implying certainty, Marlow's comments celebrate uncertainty, as if to support Carlyle's idea of symbol, which conceals as it reveals. The emphasis upon enigma that Leavis finds lamentable is not there to make a virtue of ignorance. Not only the heart of Marlow's darkness, it is also a consequence of his symbolist position. For romantic symbolists there can be no definite conclusions; and however certain Marlow may be about some images, his tale, as listening Conrad says, is "inconclusive."

Imagery of dark and light, by which the voice of the *Narcissus* expresses his uncertainties, is also useful to Marlow. Civilization is light and the forest dark; but darkness and light are always shifting and ambiguous. What seems dark may prove light and what seems light, dark; or else, mixed, they may compose the universal "grayness" that he dreads. Acclaiming light, he faces darkness; but a growing conviction that the darkness of Kurtz and the forest may be his own or that in their internal and external confusion he can no longer tell light from dark is cause for anxiety and a further cause of uncertainty. Howling natives correspond to something within himself; and at the end, still professing light, he is loyal to Kurtz's darkness.

The conflict or confusion of light and dark, inviting irony, allows morality. Marlow's moral position, though seeming plainer than it is, is emphatic. Approving fidelity, duty, discipline, and order, of which rivets,[280] navigation, and light seem symbolic, he abhors dark disorder. Morality involves choice; Marlow's, however, is not between light and dark but between kinds of dark. Forced to choose between "nightmares," that of the rapacious Belgians and that of Kurtz, Marlow chooses the latter; for to him that ultimate exclamation seems "moral victory." Not only proving Kurtz's awareness of his "degradation," his "horror," agreeably corroborating Marlow's own convictions, seems also to imply the "immense darkness" of all things.

As for the ironies: ironic Marlow seems their main and their all but unconscious object. It is ironic that one so vocal should call Kurtz "a voice." There is irony (of which Marlow is also innocent) in his unquestioning acceptance of Kurtz's "horror" as a sign of grace and moral illumination. Marlow's character compels that view of it; but for all we know Kurtz is horrified because his rituals and ivory-gathering have been cut short—or he may be looking at Marlow. The principal irony in Marlow's interview with Kurtz's Intended does not consist, as Leavis thought, in Marlow's attitude toward her or in the discrepancy between her view of Kurtz and the actuality (whatever that is) but rather in the acceptance of darkness by an apostle of light. As Marlow, that apostle, enters the house of this lover of a darkness mistaken for light, darkness enters with him and grows deeper as he talks. His defense of Kurtz out of loyalty to what is perhaps his own mistaken idea of light amounts to defense of darkness and identification with Kurtz. Marlow tells a white lie to keep the Intended in the dark by preserving her light. But even this light is uncertain—as her black dress implies; and Marlow may be right in seeing her momentarily not as a creature of light and of his chivalric expectations but as the wild woman of the Congo. An irony of which Marlow is only half aware is the terrible confusion of light and dark that he reveals within himself. Darkness in white fog seems a fitting symbol.

Chivalric diminution of woman, often attributed to Conrad, is almost peculiar to Marlow. Linda, who tends the lighthouse in the dark bay, and Lena in her black dress, deceiving her man to protect him, are of a larger kind. Even the Haldin girl, also seen through Western eyes, is more nearly human than Marlow's dream of woman. Saved by ambiguity, however, from Marlow's illusion, Kurtz's Intended emerges from it to complete the exposure by standing next to Marlow's notion of her.

As Kurtz and that forest objectify what Marlow fears he has within him, so does Lord Jim. To the great company of paranoiacs, seeking in public[281] the corroboration of private worries and their dramatization, some of Conrad's best people belong, the young captain of "The Secret Sharer" among them. Exceeding him, Marlow finds doubles not only for himself but for others. As he finds doubles for himself in Kurtz and in a variety of savages, and doubles for the Intended in the wild girl and in the girl of the allegorical painting, so he finds (or fears) another double in Jim, and detects one for him in Brown. Captain Brierly affords Marlow intimations of Jim's case and of his own potentialities. That Jim is "one of us" (a broad and ambiguous reference) is the immediate cause of Marlow's concern. Seeking Jim, Marlow seeks himself again.

The case of Marlow as Jim or of Jim as Marlow challenges moral subtlety. Dumb and clearly of the right sort, Jim has a conscience bothered by lost honor—vainly and absurdly bothered, maybe, after society forgets him. Such "exquisite sensibility," shaped not only by the code of British seamen but by that of the middle class, detains

Marlow; for he shares it. Jim's heroic death, like Kurtz's "horror," seems an assurance; but even this is imperfect, and Marlow, despairing of finalities among "unanswerable questions," confesses his failure to make the necessary but tenuous distinctions between fact and imagination, truth and illusion. Convinced of the hopelessness of finding truth, Marlow pursues it nevertheless with British fortitude. The results are as inconclusive as he expects, but pleasing enigmas have been encountered in the process. The one thing certain is that Jim is part of Marlow, existing in his memory: "after all it is only through me that he exists for you." Not Jim but what Marlow makes of him is the matter before us.

Evading analysis, Jim's case invites suggestive presentation. To Marlow, equipped for presenting mysteries by objects, Jim himself is "symbolic" and so are his three jumps—one of them, like the unflown flights of Mallarmé's swan, a jump unjumped. But to present his uncertainty, Marlow has recourse again to recurrent imagery of light and dark. Jim in immaculate white against a black coast, "at the heart of a vast enigma," and appropriately under a cloud, embodies Marlow's more definite apprehension. Commonly, however, picking his way in "cross lights," he ends in a "crepuscular" place where he can no longer tell white from black. Images of cloud, veil, fog support this grey confusion as he quests, like Wallace Stevens' guitarist, for "things exactly as they are." Marlow's view of Jim is "like those glimpses through the shifting rents in a thick fog." Though some of Marlow's images are narrowly assigned (the guano[282] island and the ring, for example), most, like the cloven peaks with the moon rising from its grave, are suitably imprecise.

As he tells us of his quest, Marlow pauses to philosophize in his bumbling fashion about the nature of things; but feeling inadequate, he consults Stein, who, however, is less philosophical than oracular, and, like most oracles, enigmatic. This collector of insects uses the butterfly to enlighten and perplex Marlow. A "gorgeous object" on its heap of dirt, captured under fire, Stein's butterfly becomes for Marlow a focal symbol. For us as well its meaning is uncertain; yet it seems somehow to include most of Marlow's concerns and those of Jim. As this lovely thing is Stein's object, so it is Jim's ideal and Marlow's Jim. Sudden challenge, success, reality and dream, dirt and beauty—all things seem embodied here. Maybe "romantic" Jim catches his butterfly at last, but we may wonder if Marlow catches his.

Stein's "destructive element," seeming easier than his butterfly, proves no less difficult. In its context, the "element" refers to dream or romantic illusion; but since this element is the sea and that is commonly an image of reality, the immersion commended by Marlow's philosopher is ambiguous. (Digression: Talking of a man immersed in that element, Stein seems to have provided Eliot with the ending of "Prufrock": "If he tries to climb out into the air . . . he drowns.") Stein fails to tell us, but we may guess, the meaning of "destructive." Marlow's response is the point: feeling enlightened, he remains confused, as Stein significantly walks from lamplight into darkness and back again. Ostensibly discursive, Stein's phrase remains a teasing metaphor; and Marlow's tale, in which Stein is an element of first importance, appears a form for presenting the process, feeling and result of man's quest for knowledge.

Of the two developments in method here, the first is more elaborate refraction, the second, complexity of structure. Up to the visit to Stein, Marlow's observations, supplemented by those of others, compose the narrative; but as Jim recedes in space, he is also distanced by the intervention of many minds. The results, as memories and fancies trouble fact, are increasing uncertainty and the enlargement of Marlow, who as collector and arranger, becomes more massively the heart of his tale and all we know for sure. As for structure: though Marlow plays with temporal sequence at one point in "Heart of Darkness," it is not until *Lord Jim* that he wins freedom from time.

The "time shift" or the "working backwards and forwards in time"[283] that Conrad and Ford devised together about this time, puts drama, expressiveness, artful juxtaposition, and disclosure ahead of normal order. Ford accounts for such disordering (at the beginning of Part Four of *The Good Soldier,* for example) on grounds of verisimilitude: it is the way a man tells a story—and maybe the way, if a detective, he comes upon its parts. But in "Heart of Darkness" Marlow, speaking of "truth stripped of its cloak of time," implies a more philosophical purpose. Whatever the purpose, the effect is plain. A narrator who scrambles times, finds matter less important than its arranger. No longer itself, moreover, matter becomes things for arrangement, for abstraction. As Picasso rearranged noses, breasts, and eyes to express his idea, so Marlow his less immediate materials.

If Marlow, more than an amateur philosopher, is a kind of artist and if his stories display the artist at work, another meaning of Stein's butterfly is relevant and functional. Stein describes his insect as a thing of accuracy and harmony, balancing colossal forces—as a work of art, in short, created by nature, "the great artist." Among the correspondences offered by that symbol, then, is this: Marlow, not only like a hunter of butterflies, is like their creator. That he fails to see this application of Stein's loaded image is probable; but that Conrad had it in mind and reserved it for development in *Chance* is not unlikely.

Conrad had put Marlow aside for many years before he got around to this. Always experimental and maybe tired of that mask, he tried other ways of presenting vision, among them a return to omniscience in *The Secret Agent.* Three observers, one exposing himself to irony, complicate the general objectivity of *Nostromo.* The effect of these returns to earlier technique is emphasis on things as they are, not on what is made of them. Maybe concern with the world of politics, which Marlow's ruminations could only diminish, accounts for this change. With *Under Western Eyes,* where society is also important, Conrad turned (while writing *Chance*) to an observer, one who is too objective and impersonal, however, to have much in common with Marlow. Whereas he looks in, those Western eyes look out. Why Conrad came back to Marlow in *Chance* is the problem. His interests are moral and philosophical. Here, beyond his depth in a psychological muddle that invites Freud, Marlow seems ill adapted for his apparent role. ("Morbid psychology," said Conrad in a letter of 1908, while writing *Chance,* "is a perfectly legitimate subject for an artist's genius. But not for a moralist.") But Marlow is excellently adapted for[284] what I think his actual role. Apparently more or less indifferent to Flora and Anthony (as we too must be), Conrad centers his interest in Marlow again—this time in another aspect. He is here, I think, to show what he does with this trivial matter, how, in particular, he gives it body and shape, how his creative imagination works. I think that *Chance* is Conrad's portrait of the artist. This seems the only justification for what, unless Marlow's method and construction are central, must be counted tedious. Henry James's praise of *Chance* for doing what requires most doing seems recognition of Conrad and, by dramatic extension, of Marlow as fellow craftsmen.

No longer driven by anxiety about himself, moved now by detached curiosity, a matchmaker's sentiment, and a surviving interest in unjumped jumps, Marlow is concerned for the first time with what he admits is none of his business. Appropriately, he is more distant than ever from his ostensible object, an object so attenuated and transformed by refractions as to make the complex refractions of *Lord Jim* seem elementary. At one point Conrad tells us what Marlow tells him of what Powell has told him of what Franklin has told him of what the Ship-keeper has told him of Flora. Almost never around at critical moments and increasingly indifferent to fact, Marlow calls upon imagination (a faculty he once denied having) for what may have happened. Emphasis, falling no longer on what he makes of a problem, falls now on what he makes. His structure, created by the imagination from almost nothing, is a glittering solid composed of method, an abstraction, like those poems in which Mallarmé elaborately celebrates nothing. Art, despite the Preface to the *Nigger,* is here for art's sake alone. Constructing this autonomous thing, Marlow is uncertain no more. There are no enigmas left; for, having made everything, he knows it. An observer still, he observes what he has made—like that aesthetic god of Stephen Dedalus, paring nails, sitting above his creation, contemplating it. There is nothing more for Marlow.[285]

MARLOW AND CONRAD*

Marvin Mudrick

"Amy Foster" contains one of Conrad's solemn, ruminative, above all experienced pipe-smoking narrators, unqualifiedly to be trusted, whose every word and motion, weighted with some meaning or other, hold the listener—and presumably the reader—in awed silence. The archetype is Marlow in *Heart of Darkness,* and here is a sample of Conrad's catch-all symbolism in presenting him:

> "... I couldn't have felt more of lonely desolation somehow, had I been robbed of a belief or missed my destiny in life."...
>
> There was a pause of profound stillness, then a match flared, and Marlow's lean face appeared, worn, hollow, with downward folds and dropped eyelids, with an aspect of concentrated attention; and as he took vigorous draws at his pipe, it seemed to retreat and advance out of the night in the regular flicker of the tiny flame. The match went out.

Apart from the author's rib-cracking nudges at us with his light-and-dark symbolism, this is Sherlock Holmes, that bundle of bogus-heroic gestures, mesmerizing a party of Watsons by the mere fact of his existence. Dr. Kennedy, in "Amy Foster", differs from Marlow only in profession; he too is supposed to unman the reader by the force of his presence, and he is impelled by the same urge to generalize, with the aid of the vaguest and most pretentious images, or anything whatever. . . .[422]

[Conrad uses long parentheses of scene-painting in "Amy Foster"] to set up in the reader a vibration to the "infinite" and "universal" implications of the story (before it has been told); to justify, by a context of facile immensities, the doctor's undocumented big words and big ideas; but we do not yet have, and shall not get, a story which in solidity of detail and in scope of characterization can sustain any such imputation of largeness and universality. What we are, in short, getting is "poetry" (from Mr. Zabel's "poet in fiction"), or rather movie music from the woodwinds: Dr. Kennedy pauses to let the universe, paying

---

* Reprinted from "Conrad and the Terms of Modern Criticism," *The Hudson Review,* Vol. VII, No. 3 (Autumn, 1954), 419-426. Copyright 1954 by The Hudson Review, Inc. By permission of the publisher. [Title mine. Ed.]

its respects, furnish the atmosphere—these gassily lyric large back-to-the-farm images—for his unqualifiable wisdom.

Conrad, and the doctor (Conrad's famous manipulation of point of view consists not infrequently in his providing himself with an identical twin named Marlow or Kennedy), make much of the words "mystery" and "truth". We are informed that "there is a particle of a general truth in every mystery"; and that, as for Amy's imagination, "How ... [it] came to her ... is an inscrutable mystery". To proclaim mystery, inscrutable or otherwise, is easy; to persuade us to suspend our disbelief in it—except as a pseudo-metaphysical indulgence—the author may reasonably be required to circumscribe it by fact and detail as closely as possible, if only to help us in estimating its magnitude. The mystery invoked in "Amy Foster", however, evaporates untested into pathos and obscurity, the obscurer the better. . . . The relationship of Amy and Yanko is explicable in terms lamentably less high-flown and more earthy than Conrad seems capable of imagining, it is in fact not, as Conrad presents it, mysterious at all, but only anecdotally interesting, rather like a "true story" whose interest depends on its being true. The mystery is that Conrad loads his little anecdote with such disproportionate, resolutely tasteless rhetoric. . . .[423]

*. . . [In *Heart of Darkness*] the problem is, of course, Kurtz. It is when we are on the verge of meeting Kurtz that Marlow's "inconceivables" and "impenetrables" begin to multiply at an alarming rate; it is when we have already met him that we are urged to observe "smiles of indefinable meaning" and to hear about "unspeakable rites.". . .[551]

The problem, as Conrad sets it up, is to persuade the reader—by epithets, exclamations, ironies, by every technical obliquity—into an hallucinated awareness of the unplumbable depravity, the primal unanalyzable evil implicit in Kurtz's reversion to the jungle from the high moral sentiments of his report. . . . Unhappily, though, the effect of even this minor irony is to bring to mind and penetrate Conrad's magazine-writer style as well as the hollowness of Kurtz's sentiments. Besides, Kurtz's sentiments must, to help justify the fuss Conrad makes about their author, radiate at least a rhetorical energy; yet all Conrad gives us of the report is a phrase or two of mealy-mouthed reformist exhortation that would not do credit to a Maugham missionary let alone the "extraordinary man" Kurtz is supposed by all accounts to be, so that the "irony" of the scrawled outcry at the end of

* Reprinted from "The Originality of Conrad," *The Hudson Review*, Vol. XI, No. 4 (Winter, 1958-59), 545-553. Copyright 1959 by The Hudson Review, Inc. By permission of the publisher. [Title mine. Ed.]

the report—"Exterminate the brutes!"—is about as subtle and un expected as the missionary's falling for the local call-girl.

In the effort to establish for Kurtz an opaque and terrifying magnitude, Conrad tends to rely more and more oppressively on these pat ironies. . . . And if the culminating irony of the narrative, Marlow's interview with[551] Kurtz's Intended, is expertly anticipated long before, when Marlow remarks—"You know I hate, detest, and can't bear a lie.". . . —it is all the more disheartening, after such anticipation, to encounter in that interview sighs, heart stoppings, chill grips in the chests, exultations, the cheaply ironic double-talk . . . as well as the sentimental lie that provokes not only her " 'cry of inconceivable triumph and of unspeakable pain' " but the final cheap irony (" ' "I knew it—I was sure!" She knew. She was sure.' ")—a jumble of melodramatic tricks so unabashed and so strategic that in any less reputable writer they might well be critically regarded as earning for the work an instant oblivion.

Still, in *Heart of Darkness* at least, Conrad is neither cynical nor laxly sentimental in his failure of imagination and corresponding failure of technique. . . . The sense of evil he must somehow project exceeds his capacity for imagining it; he strains into badness while reaching for verifications of a great and somber theme that is beyond his own very considerable powers. . . .[552]

[Nevertheless,] it is one of the great originals of literature. After *Heart of Darkness* the craftsman in fiction could never again be unaware of the moral resources inherent in every recorded sensation, or insensitive to the need of making the most precise record possible of every sensation: what now appears an immemorial cliché of the craft of fiction has a date as recent as the turn of the century. If Conrad was never quite equal to his own originality, he was at least the first to designate it as a new province of possibilities for the novelist; and, in *Heart of Darkness,* the first to suggest, by large and compelling partial proof, the intensity of moral illumination that a devoted attention to its demands might generate. The suggestion was an historical event: for good or bad novelists alike, irreversible. After *Heart of Darkness,* the recorded moment—the word—was irrecoverably symbol.[553]

MYTHIC AND LITERARY PARALLELS: THE FRAMEWORK

CONRAD'S UNDERWORLD*

Robert O. Evans

When T. S. Eliot prefaced "The Hollow Men" with the memorable, if brief, quotation from Conrad's *Heart of Darkness,* "Mistah Kurtz—he dead," he was commenting, for his own reasons, on the finality of Kurtz's descent into the underworld, much as preachers have been known to indicate Hell as the reward for sinful life. But the poem does not really deal much with "lost, violent souls," but rather with the "stuffed men," a category to which Conrad's Marlow perhaps belonged before he made his journey up the great river in Hades. It is not entirely clear from the story whether Kurtz also began as one of the "hollow men" or not, but that point is not important, for Conrad's hero is Marlow, and the story deals with change in his character. Kurtz enters the picture, as it were, only incidentally at the end as an agent in Marlow's acquisition of knowledge. *The Heart of Darkness,* like Eliot's poem, is written for the futile ones "gathered on this beach of the tumid river"; it is not much concerned with eternal damnation in the sense that the inhabitants of Dante's *Inferno* are dead and have gathered their deserts. The story is developed in terms of symbols, and it is, of course, not always possible to distinguish a clear separation between the symbolic and literal levels of meaning. For instance, Kurtz is plainly alive when Marlow begins his journey and still alive when Marlow reaches him, but symbolically there is no doubt that he is the arch-inhabitant of Hell or that Marlow, too, has been journeying through Hell, much as Dante did in the *Inferno.* Superficially there are differences; for example, Marlow travels alone while Dante had Virgil for his guide. But that Africa represents Hell and the great river, Acheron, Phlegethon, Styx, or all the rivers of Hell together is a traditional interpretation of the story.

Recently Miss Lillian Feder has pointed out a number of significant parallels with Virgil's descent in the sixth book of the *Aeneid,*[1]

* Reprinted from *Modern Fiction Studies,* II (May, 1956) by permission of the copyright owners, Purdue Research Foundation.

1 "Marlow's Descent into Hell," *Nineteenth-Century Fiction,* IX (March, 1955), 280-292.

but *The Heart of Darkness* is more than a reworking of an old theme in modern guise. There is no question that Conrad employed epic machinery borrowed from Virgil. Essentially the story is neither a recitation of Kurtz's awful degradation nor the simple history of Marlow's enlightenment. It is a journey through the underworld, for purposes of instruction as well as entertainment, calculated to bring into focus Conrad's moral vision, as it affects the mass of humanity struggling on the brink of the "tumid river." The story is really concerned with modern ethical and spiritual values and has far more significance for the reader than any transmutation of Virgil's descent could have. Clearly it was not possible for Conrad, writing in the twentieth century, to view the world with a disregard for Christian ethics, as Virgil had to do. Accordingly one would expect Conrad to have a deeper significance than Virgil. Moreover, as one of his main themes, the descent into Hell, was not Virgil's exclusive property, it would not seem likely that Conrad should owe Virgil more than Dante, or even Milton. I shall attempt to show that he did in fact make extensive use of the *Inferno* in the general structure of the story, and by his adoption of epic techniques[56] and epic themes he accomplished something almost unique in the short story, or novelette. *The Heart of Darkness* is not the apex of a genre but rather a special use of form towards which Conrad had been painfully working in order to express his particular, ethical view of the universe.

It is not necessary to review the broad parallels with the *Aeneid* here. Much of the Virgilian machinery is commonplace anyhow. Perhaps it is an overstatement of the case to point out, as Miss Feder does, that when "Aeneas first enters Hades, Virgil compares the underworld with a forest (VI, 270-271)," for Dante, too, woke to find himself "lost in a dark wood." The rivers of Hell belong to every myth. The knitters of black wool in the company offices may resemble the Cumaean Sibyl, but they are not entirely unlike Milton's guardians, Sin and Death, and the difference in their ages suggests such a relationship. Nevertheless, Conrad does appear to draw on Virgil as well as other sources. He may use a Latin farewell, "Ave! old knitter of black wool," but he also makes statements like Marlow's, that he felt as if he "were about to set off for the center of the earth," a direction that seems more closely related to Dante's cosmology than to Virgil's.

From the beginning of the story there is little question where Marlow's journey will lead him, but, as Miss Feder says, the Hell into which Marlow descends is legendary rather than an actual place. This problem of how to give Hell being without the same sense of existence that Dante experienced is one of the most difficult a modern artist can face. One knows it is there, but where exactly is it? As Graham Greene recognized, "there are a thousand names for it, King Solomon's mines, the 'heart of darkness' if one is romantically inclined . . . [etc.]" (*Journey Without Maps,* p. 8). Conrad solves his enigma by deft manipulation of symbols and imagery. Marlow, looking at a map of his projected journey, remarks that he is "going into the yellow—dead in the center." But as the symbolic level of meaning shifts slightly, most of the other references to Hell are described as properly black. Marlow's appointment is to replace a man who was killed in an argument over two "black hens," an image carefully related to the two females that surround Kurtz. The knitters are working "black wool." Marlow's first contact with the natives is with black men, whose loins are bound in "black rags." The single, outstanding descriptive detail about the European traders is their "black mustaches." The background of Kurtz's mysterious painting was "almost black—somber." The river is black; "there were shiny patches on the black creek." Even the natives' confidence is a "black display." Thoughts are black. And again, later, the men themselves are no more than grains of sand in a "black Sahara." Conrad colors Hell rightly but only after making it clear, partly through imagery, that it is not a literal place.

Perhaps the author's use of the *Inferno* is not quite so explicit as that of the *Aeneid,* but it is probably more important to the development of the story. In the first place, besides being shorter, Virgil's journey is ideologically simpler than Dante's, and the progression into the underworld in the sixth book of the *Aeneid* is accomplished at a fairly steady rate, while Dante's journey is interrupted; that is, he travels and then stops and comments, continues, and so on. In these respects *The Heart of Darkness* is more closely modelled on the Italian epic than on the Latin original. But it is the epic nature of the story that is important; throughout Conrad makes considerable use of epic machinery. For example, the story begins *in media res,* but the scene on shipboard in the estuary of the Thames, in sharp contrast to the opening scene of, say, Galsworthy's[57] *The Apple Tree,* is no mere enveloping action; it is as much an integral portion of the story as the initial scene of the *Odyssey*. Moreover, as Conrad's vision is ethical, he takes pains to connect the Thames with the great river in Africa, thus implying that Marlow's experience is meaningful for the modern world. But Conrad does not allow his meaning to rest on a subtle implication; he troubles to explain that this is no simple sea-yarn. It lacks, he says, the "direct simplicity, the whole meaning of which lies within the shell of a cracked nut . . . Marlow was not typical [i.e. of the spinners of sea stories]." This is also a clear statement that the story must not be read literally. Despite the complex symbolism almost everything is in the foreground; Conrad takes few chances on the readers' imaginations. He once said that it was the duty of the artist to make the reader "see." An early example of his foreground technique occurs when he has Marlow inform the assembled company that the Thames, too, "has been one of the dark places of the earth." A veneer of civilization has perhaps brought some light to England, but I am inclined to believe that Conrad's choice of tense, *has been,* is at least partly ironical, for later, though he specifically avoids attacking British civilization in this story, it becomes clear that his opinion of western culture is not high. Readers of *Victory* may recall how stinging he could be when he wished. But the artistic technique of placing nearly everything in the foreground may, in some fashion, be responsible for the shallow interpretation of the story that has arisen, that it is little more than an attack on British imperialism. I have no doubt that Conrad lacked enthusiasm for colonial policy, as his Congo diary reveals, but in this work he specifically avoids attacking it.

Instead he uses epic machinery to elucidate his ethical purpose. He goes to what might have been, in the hands of a lesser artist, absurd lengths to incorporate epic qualities. For example, near the beginning of the story there is the familiar list of ships, starting with the *Golden Hind* but ending, significantly I think, with *Erebus* and *Terror*. These men-of-war are appropriate for *The Heart of Darkness*. Still, it is interesting to compare the passage with Masefield's realistic poem. Conrad has nothing to say here about the "dirty British coaster . . . laden with pig iron and cheap tin trays." As with colonial policy, he is concerned with the shabbiness of modern life only where it cuts across his moral vision.

It is not easy to determine exactly how closely Conrad relied on Dante. I do not mean to imply that he has slavishly enlisted under any master, but the structure of *The Heart of Darkness*, at least from the moment of Marlow's arrival at the first station on the African coast, closely resembles a skeletalized version of the *Inferno*. And even prior to Marlow's landing the characters in the story would appear to fit nicely into Dante's threshold to Hell. Perhaps the knitters of black wool are slightly misplaced; Dante might have introduced them earlier. The directors themselves, though they do not realize it, belong in the Vestibule, as men whose lives have warranted neither great infamy nor great praise. Seamen who have abandoned the sea, they are now businessmen. They seem to fit, as Miss Sayers says, into "the Vestibule . . . the abode of the weather-cock mind, the vague tolerance which will neither approve nor condemn, the cautious cowardice for which no decision is ever final." Conrad does not openly lay these charges on the directors, for the initial scene is one of the few places in the story where everything is not in the foreground. But of the whole group only Marlow is shown to have adhered to the true purpose of life, the development of ethical insight, and he is the only one who still follows the sea, a distinction of symbolic importance. Actually Marlow has little space to devote to the directors;[58] they serve as Marlow's audience, but they are not the audience the author is trying to convince. *The Heart of Darkness* is not their story. They are really incapable of understanding it, as Conrad suggests when he puts in the narrator's mouth the insipid remark, "we knew we were fated . . . to hear about one of Marlow's *inconclusive* experiences" (italics mine). But at least they are capable of sensing something special about Marlow, for the same speaker relates that Marlow "had the pose of a Buddha preaching in European clothes and without a lotus flower." This is plain description of Marlow's mission.

The continentals, too, are "hollow men" living in or near the Vestibule, except perhaps for the guardians. Some, of course, are better than others. The doctor, like the narrator on the *Nellie,* has some realization of the importance of Marlow's journey, shown by his farewell, "Du calme, du calme. Adieu." The women in the story, beginning with Marlow's aunt, are not really damned but live in an unreal world of their own, incapable of understanding. Miss Feder has suggested that Kurtz's fiancee may occupy a special corner of Hades because she is related, through imagery, to Kurtz and, she says, has no separate existence apart from him. It is quite true that when the reader meets her she appears dressed in black, but I do not think the color alone enough to consign her to Hell. She is mourning for Kurtz in a mistaken, over-sentimental but not abnormal fashion. And her existence does not entirely depend on him. Conrad uses her primarily for an agent in Marlow's eventual discovery of the ethical nature of life. Structurally she is bound to Marlow. Symbolically Conrad simplified Marlow's problems until they are mostly bound in the experience of falsehood. The most distasteful action Marlow is capable of is a lie, but twice he is brought to tell one. On the first occasion he lies for practical reasons in order to obtain rivets to repair the steamer, symbolizing dishonesty in the course of the normal business of life. Of course, the lie is successful. But later, when he visits Kurtz's "Intended," Marlow tells another lie, this time with no ulterior motive, and this selfless though intrinsically sinful action, a sort of parable, completes his moral vision. Conrad needs the fiancee for Marlow far more than he does to explain Kurtz's presence in Africa. She, like Marlow's aunt, simply does not understand the real world. The women of this story live in a special, mythical realm of their own.

The close structural parallel between *The Heart of Darkness* and the *Inferno* is not explicit at the Vestibule stage. Moreover, Dante borrowed the Vestibule from Virgil, though Conrad's tenants resemble Dante's far more than the Latin poet's. But from the landing in Africa and Marlow's descent into Limbo the relationship becomes unmistakable. Immediately preceding the real descent, Conrad devotes several paragraphs to explanation, in symbolic terms, of his special Hades. He carefully separates Africa from modern civilization by describing machinery rusting uselessly on a hillside. Graham Greene, faced with a similar need himself when he wrote *Journey Without Maps,* showed acute sympathy for Conrad's problem. Describing his own feelings he wrote, "A quality of darkness is needed, of the inexplicable . . . one sees . . . to what peril of extinction centuries of cerebration have brought us." Conrad, too, gives Marlow a preconception of what he would have to face: "I foresaw that in the blinding sunshine of that land I would become acquainted with a flabby, pretending, weak-eyed devil of a rapacious and pitiless folly." The "blinding sunshine," related to the "yellow" of the map, stresses the reality that supplies vitality to the myth.[59]

Next Conrad turns to Marlow's meeting with the Chief Accountant, noteworthy for his gentle annoyance at having his work disturbed by a dying man on a litter placed in the office with him. The accountant is beyond the violence and the brutality. He keeps up appearances. He does not really suffer. Accordingly, he resembles Dante's tenants who have "sinned not; yet their merit lacked its chiefest / / Fulfillment, lacking baptism, which is / / The gateway to the faith which thou believest." The accountant belongs in Limbo.

From the coast up the river to the second station the characters in the story closely resemble the inhabitants of Upper Hell. Conrad does not follow Dante's eschatology strictly, but certainly the ivory traders belong with the lustful, gluttonous, wrathful. The second station is the abode of the fraudulent, through which blows, appropriately, "a taint of imbecile rapacity . . . like a whiff from some corpse." The idea is Dante's; the passage actually may have been drawn from a notation in the *Congo Diary,* "saw at a camp place the dead body of a Backongo. Shot? Horrid smell." He describes the station at length, its "air of plotting, [where the inhabitants] intrigued and slandered and hated each other," in terms that would be appropriate for Dante's City of Dis, that domain in the *Inferno* of those whose sins of violence and fraud involve exercise of the will.

From the second station on, up the river to Kurtz's outpost, Conrad carefully draws his characters as if they now inhabited Nether Hell. Nevertheless there is a fundamental difference between *The Heart of Darkness* and the *Inferno* at this stage. The inhabitants of Conrad's City of Dis actually travel further into the underworld; Dante's damned are fixed. I think this is an essential part of Conrad's solution to the problem of making Hell real though not actual. Moreover, the geography of Hell is, naturally, somewhat altered. As Marlow travels up the river on the steam launch, the natives are literally downtrodden blacks, but they resemble those who are violent against their neighbors. In fact, violence is one of their few distinguishing characteristics. The traders, now called Pilgrims primarily because they move about in Hell, take on the attributes of the circles they have entered. They too become violent, firing wickedly if ineffectually into the underbrush. The Russian trader that Marlow and his company encounter does seem slightly out of place in terms of Dante's scheme, for he appears to be a heretic. Conrad actually calls him a "harlequin," a verbal resemblance that is perhaps more than coincidental. He is not himself one of the violent; his real sin is accepting Kurtz as a false god. Their relationship is also in the foreground, though Conrad does not enlarge upon it. The trader merely remarks of Kurtz, "This man has enlarged my mind," suggesting intellectual sin, which heresy is. Conrad leaves little doubt about their relations in the readers' minds. The trader has not meditated about his connection with Kurtz; "it came to him, and he accepted it with a sort of eager fatalism." Marlow explains, "I must say that to me it appeared about the most dangerous thing in every way he had come upon so far." A writer could scarcely leave less to the imagination. Then, at the center of the underworld, Conrad presents Kurtz, perhaps something of a disappointment, because he does nothing but talk and die, to a reader schooled on the modern short story. But Kurtz fits Dante's scheme perfectly, as traitor to kindred, having put behind him all relations with Europe, to country, having abandoned even the platitudinous lip-service to the civilizing ideal upheld by the others, to guests, having turned upon the trader who nursed him, to God, having set himself up as a "graven image" in the center of Hades. In short Kurtz is the living Lucifer even without the unspeakable rites mentioned by Marlow.[60]

His native queen, on the other hand, is an emendation to the complicated Dante-like system, though she completes Kurtz's degradation. In a sense she is not materially different from the aunt and the fiancee. In her ambitious dreams, which differ from theirs only because she is more primitive, she is out of touch with the real world. Another structural difference between the two works seems to lie in the fact that Conrad neglected the final circle of Dante's Hell, the frozen Lake of Cocytus. But Conrad's Hell is mythical. Literally Kurtz was alive when Marlow reached him. Death was still his immediate future, and perhaps he is not symbolically fixed in ice, like the Alberti brothers, because Conrad wished to suggest that evil as he was a still worse fate awaited him. His final words, "the horror, the horror," may not only refer back to his Satanic service but may also look ahead to an everlasting horror.

I have devoted some time to showing that the structural basis of *The Heart of Darkness* resembles that of the *Inferno*. As Marlow descends deeper into Hades, he meets characters whose sins loosely correspond with those in the Italian epic. But Conrad by no means runs through the list of the seven deadly sins with their numerous subdivisions. In fact he does not conceive evil dialectically, but he roughly follows a tripartite division of sin of his own making, materially different from but not certainly related to the commonplace medieval conception. At the first station is the accountant, doomed but not suffering, in Limbo; at the next, the City of Dis, the ivory traders much as Dante would have treated them; finally, Kurtz, Lucifer himself, taking on the attributes of all the sins in which he has participated. Such a conception would be familiar to Dante, for superimposed on the complicated structure of his Hell is the threefold machinery of Vestibule, Upper Hell, Nether Hell. Conrad's structure is epic; he was not writing the usual sort of short story. As Miss Feder recognizes, he was heroically depicting "Marlow's discovery of evil and the responsibilities to himself and to others which this knowledge places upon him."

On the other hand, Miss Feder contends that Conrad employed the descent into Hell theme, at least to some extent, in order to "build up suspense, to tell the reader indirectly that this is no ordinary voyage." The voyage is certainly extraordinary, but, as I have pointed out, Conrad does not impart this information through implication. He states it so plainly and so often that the reader can scarcely mistake his meaning. Nor can I agree that the epic theme is employed to develop suspense. As I have shown, Conrad takes pains to adhere to epic structure, patterned after that of the *Inferno*. Suspense is a very slight element in both the classical epic and in Dante and of minor importance in *The Heart of Darkness*. Conrad's goal, as Schiller said of Homer, is "already present in every point of his progress." From the first scene on the deck of the cruising yawl, *Nellie,* the reader is aware —even before the descent into Hell theme commences—that he is not listening to an ordinary sea-yarn. Marlow is no common sailor, any more than Christ's disciples were. He is described as sitting "cross-legged right aft . . . resembling an idol." The initial action is connected chronologically, through the epic list of ships, with heroic actions of the past. The Thames is geographically connected with all the other waters of the world and mythologically with the underworld. The preliminary scene, no mere enveloping action calculated to add verisimilitude, tends to do away with suspense.

In a geographical sense as well the story progresses from incident through journey to further incident, avoiding climax by diversions of great intrinsic value, much as Dante progresses through the various circles of Hell. And[61] because of this technique few experienced readers are likely to find themselves breathless as they journey with Conrad into the dark continent. The strength of the story lies not in the suspense it develops but in the power of its clear moral insight and in the readers' realization that they, too, could perhaps under trial follow in Marlow's footsteps. As Graham Greene has remarked, "Here you could measure what civilization was worth."

Conrad does not always employ this technique. *Victory,* for example, develops suspense much as most modern novels do and even hinges in the final analysis on a gunshot. But *The Heart of Darkness* never leaves the reader in much doubt about the outcome. There is really no question that Marlow might follow the fate of Kurtz, because of the initial action, nor that Kurtz might conceivably be saved. Conrad's reader moves through the episodes much as Homer's does. Far more important than suspense is what Goethe and Schiller called the "retarding element." Erich Auerbach claims, in *Mimesis,* that suspense in the modern sense tends to rob the audience of emotional freedom; whereas the opposite technique in the epic creates it. For the development of Conrad's purpose, the promotion of ethical insight, the reader must be left emotionally free so that he can judge not only Kurtz's action but Marlow's as well, and draw the right conclusions from them. I contend that Conrad was fully aware of this problem and realized that a solution in modern, prose form was extremely difficult. Throughout his career he struggled towards an answer. *The Shadow Line* and "The Secret Sharer" are attempts in the same direction, but it was only with the happy adoption of epic technique in *The Heart of Darkness,* based largely on the descent into Hell theme which Conrad borrowed from Dante and Virgil, that he achieved complete success.[62]

THE LOTUS POSTURE AND "THE HEART OF DARKNESS"*

William Bysshe Stein

Although Robert O. Evans' "Conrad's Underground" offers some interesting "epic" parallels to *The Heart of Darkness,* it fails, I think, to cope with the moral experience in terms of the structure of the story. While I will not deny that there is a rough development of the myth of the descent into the underworld, this pattern of action cannot be viewed by itself and in itself. It must, rather, be seen in the Jamesian frame Conrad provides. Mr. Evans, to be sure, takes note of this important element of structure, but unfortunately he does not consider it to have a function. I refer, of course, to the Buddha tableaux, the positioning of which cannot be ignored, the two at the beginning, the one near the middle, and the other in the final paragraph of the work.

Mr. Evans even goes so far as to introduce his fragmentary citations from the tableaux into the context of Marlow's recital; actually they belong to the perspective of the first person narrator who acquaints us with the adventurer. Conrad deliberately restricts them to the vision of the latter because, as Mr. Evans is aware, he is one of the four auditors who cannot possibly understand the significance of a subtle spiritual voyage. All four are blinded by their infatuation with the material aspects of the world. Yet, as I shall show, the tableaux of

* Reprinted from *Modern Fiction Studies,* II (Winter, 1956-57), by permission of the copyright owners, Purdue Research Foundation.

the lotus postures instruct the reader how to interpret Marlow's descent into the underworld—his own, not Virgil's or Dante's.

Most of us, I am sure, are familiar with the stylized postures and gestures of Indian art, that is, with their appearance, not their meaning. Conrad, if we can claim Marlow as his "altar" ego, not only understood them; he believed in them. The first tableau, for instance, catches the hero in the physical position prerequisite to Yoga meditation, contemplation, and absorption. On the brink of the spiritual fulfillment that comes with self-recollection (a mode of personal salvation diametrically opposed to the Occidental belief that perfection is acquired from without, for in the Indian view the process is one of bringing into consciousness what lies in a dormant and quiescent state, the timeless reality of one's being) Marlow's lotus posture shows he is ready to engage in an exercise of intense introspection; he is ready to contemplate the chaos out of which order or cosmos comes: "Marlow sat *cross-legged* right aft. . . . He had *sunken cheeks, a yellow complexion, a straight back,* an *ascetic aspect,* and *with his arms dropped, the palms of hands outward,* resembled an idol (italics are mine)." This description gives evidence of the self-mortification, the denial of the tyranny of physical matter, which precedes the introversion of consciousness. And surely the combination of gestures by the limbs is enough to command alert attention; or is Conrad, like Marlow, addressing himself to the inadvertent curiosity of a[235] reader as dull as the observer? In effect, it seems to me that Conrad in setting up this tableau is ridiculing the moral complacency which, confronted by a form of religious discipline older by far than Christianity, is so incapable of expanding its understanding.

A similar irony asserts itself in the next tableau, for again Marlow's posture is the occasion for deprecation: "he had the pose of a Buddha preaching in European clothes and without a lotus-flower." But while we are engaged in a consideration of these blind impeachments, let us not forget that the springboard for Mr. Evans' treatment of the story as epic is this same narrative voice. It is he who invokes the romance of the sea: the *Golden Hind,* the *Erebus,* and the *Terror.* If he is also a representative of the class Conrad is mocking, then Mr. Evans is not justified in citing these images in proof of his thesis.

Indeed, the basic irony of *The Heart of Darkness* resides in the preoccupation of Marlow's auditors with the external aspects of the descent into the African underworld. Conrad's repetition of the word "meditation" is a rubric here. He wishes to stress that Marlow's journey is only important to the degree that he can vicariously relive Kurtz's lapse into primitive degradation. This emphasis is likewise affirmed in Marlow's virtual obsession with Kurtz, the passionate interest in the man that grew as he proceeded towards the inner station. It is also manifest in Marlow's meticulous recreation of every facet of his trip, beginning with the interview on the continent. This recapitulation is necessary if he is to follow Kurtz's soul to the brink of utter damnation. After all, the latter's enlightenment consists of the sudden insight into his appalling inhumanity: " 'the horror' " and the "depths of his meanness." And Marlow leaves no doubt that he himself is party to the experience: "But his soul was mad. Being alone in the wilderness, it had looked within itself, and, by heavens! I tell you, it had gone mad. I had—for my sins, I suppose—*to go through the ordeal of looking into it myself* (italics mine)." But, of course, the nature of his enlightenment is different from Kurtz's, and at this point his lotus posture defines itself.

In an exercise of arduous spiritual discipline, symbolized in his physical bearing and studied introversion, "worn, hollow, with downward folds and drooped eyelids, with an aspect of concentrated attention," he lives through, to the very limit, a particular role in life. And in suffering its consequences, he fathoms and exhausts its contents. He descends into his own hell of fear, desire, and fleshly limitations, bearing all the suffering of his attachment to matter. At the last moment, he resists the attraction which Kurtz acknowledges. He breaks free from the forces of the flesh. With the story of his spiritual journey told, he sits in the inturned lotus posture, detached from the conditions, the victories, and the vicissitudes of time: "Marlow ceased, sat apart, indistinct and silent, in the pose of the meditating Buddha." And, as before, the narrator-observer is beguiled by outward appearance. Marlow has voyaged alone among the temptations which entangle man in time. He has not communicated with his auditors. He stands apart from them, the anonymous ascetic, cleansed and purged by his introspective ordeal.[236]

This is all that Conrad tells the reader. The symbolic consecration to the ideal of Buddhahood constitutes the refinement of the experience in the heart of darkness. Whatever spiritual implications one finds in the story must be based on the tableaux. In effect, we have journeyed along "the way of the Bodhisattva." We have stood on the brink of time and eternity with Kurtz and Marlow, and we have seen the latter transcend this pair of opposites. We have also witnessed his triumph over inward suffering and toil. Although qualified to enter nirvana, like the true Bodhisattva, Marlow remains in the world to work for the salvation of all people. In his stage of enlightenment he teaches what his descent into the imperfections of the human soul has taught him —egoless compassion. Cancelling out all personal desire and fear, he has made available to humanity the gift of complete renunciation. To every suffering, striving creature, trapped in the karmic processes (enslavement to matter), he offers the inexhaustible wisdom of selflessness.

This interpretation, without the slightest exaggeration, emerges out of scrupulous focus on the structure of the story. A vision of spiritual reality is framed in the Buddha tableaux. Its meaning is not dependent upon any "epic" technique. If anything, consistent with Marlow's ironical attitude towards his audience, whatever parallels to the pagan and Christian underworlds that he broaches must be looked upon ironically. And here again I feel that Mr. Evans in his concern with a pattern of symbolism has slighted another of Conrad's conscious artistic practices. I refer in this instance to tone. Mr. Evans is quite aware of this device but never in the perspective of its effects upon thematic meaning. The self-mockery that pervades the Marlow recital, it seems to me, must operate to temper the ego climate of epic endeavor. Outward heroics are hardly a reflection of the compassionate Buddha.[237]

A FURTHER NOTE ON THE FUNCTION OF THE FRAME IN "HEART OF DARKNESS"*

Seymour L. Gross

Despite the frequency with which Conrad's "Heart of Darkness" has been discussed, the function of the frame in the novelette—the four men who sit on the deck of the *Nellie* and listen to Marlow's tale—has either been ignored or somewhat misconstrued. For example, Robert O. Evans in his "Conrad's Underworld" asserts that "actually Marlow [Conrad] has little space to devote to the directors. They serve as Marlow's audience, but they are not the audience the author is trying to convince. The *Heart of Darkness* is not their story. They are really incapable of understanding it, as Conrad suggests when he puts in the narrator's mouth the insipid remark, "We knew we were fated ... to hear about one of Marlow's inconclusive experiences.' "

Similarly, William Bysshe Stein, in his "The Lotus Posture and 'The Heart of Darkness,' " recognizes the moral importance of the structure of the story and interestingly explicates the Buddha imagery in the frame, but nevertheless agrees with Mr. Evans that Marlow's[167] story falls upon the spiritually deaf ears "of the four auditors who cannot possibly understand the significance of a subtle spiritual voyage."

I believe it is a mistake, however, to lump the four auditors together indiscriminately. As a matter of fact, Conrad subtly but emphatically differentiates one of the listeners—the first narrator—from

* Reprinted from *Modern Fiction Studies,* III (Summer, 1957), by permission of the copyright owners, Purdue Research Foundation.

the other three. What Evans and Stein say is true for the other three men, who, it turns out, are indeed incapable of comprehending the staggering implications of Marlow's tale. These three, in the frame, reflect all those in the actual experience—the corrupt pilgrims, the fantastic Russian, the company officials—who are unable to grasp the "hidden truth" of the moral abysm into which they have descended. For these three men, Marlow's tale (as Kurtz himself had been to the others *in* the story) is at worst ridiculous, at best an adventure story to listen to and forget. The only comment one of the three makes during the telling of Marlow's tale is "absurd," which understandably evokes from the experientially wiser Marlow the angry exclamation, "Absurd! ... This is the worst of trying to tell.... Here you all are, each moored with two good addresses, like a hulk with two anchors, a butcher round one corner, a policeman round another, excellent appetites, and temperature normal—you hear—normal from year's end to year's end. And you say, Absurd! Absurd be—exploded! Absurd!" And when the terrifying saga of human degradation and triumph is concluded, the only thing the Director can find to say is the practical but, in the context, morally obtuse comment, "We have lost the first of the ebb." This group in the frame reflects all those in the actual adventure, and by extension in life, who are "too much of a fool to go wrong—too dull even to know [they] are being assaulted by the powers of darkness."

The first narrator is something else again. He is hardly, as Mr. Stein asserts, "dull" and incorrigibly "beguiled by outward appearance," "a representative of the class Conrad is mocking." He, in the frame, stands in the same relationship to Marlow as Marlow stood to Kurtz in the actual experience. He is precisely "the audience the author is trying to convince," for he is a man, as becomes increasingly apparent, who is capable of "facing the darkness" and of accepting its black message. It is true, as Mr. Evans asserts, that his comment about Marlow's inconclusive tales is insipid; but it must be noted that this is the kind of superficiality he is capable of only *before* he has lived through Marlow's tale, just as Marlow considers his own judgment before he has lived through Kurtz as being that of "a silly little bird." Both Marlow and the first narrator, metaphorically speaking, start at the same place, take the same trip, and arrive at the same destination.

When we first meet the narrator, he is a potentially sensitive but essentially optimistic man—a man who sees and evaluates experience from a "lightened" (though hardly enlightened) point of view. Although we are told nothing directly about him, the manner in which Conrad has him describe things serves to reveal the delusion of his moral innocence, a delusion which Marlow's tale is to shatter in precisely the same way as the reality of Kurtz's degradation shattered Marlow's own "mournful and senseless delusion."[168]

The imagery of light with which the first two pages of the story are studded serves both as an index to the narrator's innocence and as an ironic prologue to Marlow's opening comment—"And this also . . . has been one of the dark places on the earth." For the first narrator, the Thames is a "benign immensity of unstained light," enveloped in a mist of "gauzy and radiant fabric"; on her "luminous" waters the sails of the barges "seemed to stand still in red clusters of canvas sharply peaked, with gleams of varnished sprits." After the day ends "in a serenity of still and exquisite brilliance," "Lights of ships moved in the fairway—a great stir of lights going up and going down." Moreover, his conception of the history of the river—which Conrad ironically comments upon in Marlow's harrowing tale of the first Romans struggle with "the fascination of the abomination"—is the epitome of bright, shadowless naiveté. For him, the history of the Thames is only "ships whose names are like jewels flashing in the night of time," carrying "bearers of a spark from the sacred fire" to glorious conquests. "What greatness had not floated on the ebb of that river. . . . The dreams of men, the seed of commonwealths, the germs of empires." Marlow is soon to give him another kind of vision of the men who go into the heart of darkness: "the growing regrets, the longing to escape, the powerless disgust, the surrender, the hate."

Although the narrator, with the others, at first merely sits back patiently to listen to Marlow's yarn, by the time Marlow has threaded his way through about a third of his experience, he suffers a severe shock to his moral equilibrium. In the symbolic darkness which has enveloped the group, Marlow becomes for the narrator "no more . . . than a voice," just as Kurtz, to Marlow, had also "presented himself as a voice." And it is a disturbing voice. "The others might have been asleep, but I was awake. I listened, I listened on the watch for the sentence, for the word, that would give me the clew to the faint uneasiness inspired by this narrative that seemed to shape itself without human lips in the heavy night air of the river." At this point, Marlow's tale seems to hold out for the narrator the promise of some moral revelation, which is exactly what Kurtz had come to represent for Marlow at an analogous point in his experience. (For example, when Marlow thinks that Kurtz is dead, he says, "I couldn't have felt more lonely desolation somehow, had I been robbed of a belief or had missed my destiny in life.")

The narrator's moral progress is completed in the final paragraph of the story. Marlow's tale of "diabolic love and unearthly hate" has literally bowed the narrator with the sheer immensity of its implications. Immediately after the Director's banal comment, he says, "I raised my head. The offing was barred by a black bank of clouds, and the tranquil waterway leading to the uttermost ends of the earth flowed somber under an overcast sky—seemed to lead into the heart of an immense darkness." The transformation has been complete: "the benign immensity of unstained light" has become "the heart of an immense darkness." Now he, like Marlow, will be set apart from all those who do not know the truth.

The recognition of the reflective function of the frame in "Heart of Darkness" not only serves to reinforce the thematic implications of the story[169] in much the same way as, for example, Gloucester's tragedy reinforces Lear's, but adds a new aspect to the work as well. That the narrator is able to arrive at his moral insight through "literature," as Marlow had arrived at his through experience, demonstrates Conrad's faith in the moral efficacy of experience through literature. Louis Armstrong once remarked that there are people who if they don't know, you can't tell them. What Conrad seems to be saying is that these people can't be told either by life or literature. It seems to me, then, that the "Heart of Darkness" is not only an enduring comment on the nature of man, but a parable on the possibilities of moral knowledge as well.[170]

THE LIE

INGRESS TO THE HEART OF DARKNESS*

Walter F. Wright

The tragedy of Kurtz and the education of Marlow fuse into one story, since for Marlow that tragedy represents his furthest penetration into the heart of darkness. As Marlow enters the forest to intercept Kurtz on the way toward the ceremonial blaze he senses the fascination which the savage ritual possesses. In the light of Conrad's other tales we know that it is because he is guided by well-established habits that he is able to complete his mission and carry Kurtz back to his cot, though not before he himself has apprehended the lure of the primitive. He has duplicated in his own experience enough of Kurtz's sensations to have good reason to wonder what is real and what is a false trick of the imagination. It was this fascination and bewilderment that Conrad aimed to suggest, and the presenting of Kurtz at the most intense moment of his yielding to it was to transcend time and bring a unity of impression.

When Marlow, soon after, hears the dying pronouncement, "the horror, the horror!" he has more than a mere intellectual awareness of what the words mean; and as we have vicariously shared Marlow's quasi-hysterical emotion on the trip toward the camp fire, we feel likewise the completeness with which Kurtz has savored degradation. He is a universal genius because he has had both the dream of sweetness and sacrifice in a cause shared by others and the disillusionment of being, in the very midst of the savage adoration, irretrievably alone, devoid of all standards, all hopes that can give him a sense of kinship with anything in the universe. Now, as he faces the last darkness of all, he cannot even know that Marlow understands and that he feels no right to condemn.[157]

. . . Conscious will was, in the novelist's opinion, not merely fallible, but often dangerous. Reliance upon it could lead one completely away from human sentiments. In "Heart of Darkness" itself Kurtz twice replies to Marlow that he is "perfectly" conscious of what he is doing; his sinister actions are deliberate. This fact does not in the least, however, mean that Conrad wished for a condition devoid of

* Reprinted by permission of the publisher from Walter F. Wright, *Romance and Tragedy in Joseph Conrad* (Lincoln: University of Nebraska Press, 1949).

will. He believed that man had the power to pursue the interpretation of experience with deliberate intent and by conscious endeavor to reduce it to proportions. The imagination would bring up the images and incidents, but the reason could help select and arrange them until they became the essence of art. In his trip up the Congo and in his rapid descent Marlow is protected by habits which tend to preserve sanity, but the experience is of the imagination and emotions. Were he to stop short with the mere sensations, he would have no power to distinguish reality from the unreal, to speculate, with touchstones for reference, about life. What we are coming to is the obvious question, If Kurtz's dictum represents the deepest penetration into one aspect of the mind, why did Conrad not stop there; why did he have Marlow tell the girl that Kurtz died pronouncing her name? Is the ending tacked on merely to relieve the horror, or has it a function in the conscious interpretation of life in the proportions of art? . . .

The fact is that Conrad, fully capable of building to a traditional climax and stopping, wanted to put Kurtz's life in the perspective which it must have for Marlow *sub*[158] *specie aeternitatis.* Marlow does not have a final answer to life, but after we have shared with him the steady penetration to the brink of degradation we have almost forgotten what life otherwise is like. It is now that Conrad's method of chronological reversal is invaluable. We are quickly returned to Europe, where the marvel of Kurtz's genius still remains, as if he had left but yesterday.

The scene in which Marlow conceals from the girl the nature of Kurtz's death is really a study of the nature of truth. If he had told the girl the simple facts, he would have acknowledged that the pilgrims in their cynicism had the truth, that goodness and faith were the unrealities. Marlow appreciates this temptation, and we are hardly to suppose that sentimental weakness makes him resist it. He does not preach to us about the wisdom he has achieved; in fact he deprecates it, and now he says merely that to tell her would be "too dark altogether." He is still perplexed as to the ethics of his deception and wishes that fate had permitted him to remain a simple reporter of incidents instead of making him struggle in the realm of human values. Yet in leaving in juxtaposition the fiancée's ideal, a matter within her own heart, and the fact of Kurtz's death, Marlow succeeds in putting before us in his inconclusive way the two extremes that can exist within the human mind, and we realize that not one, but both of these are reality.

When Marlow ends his monologue, his audience are aware that the universe around them, which, when we began the story, seemed an ordinary, familiar thing, with suns rising and setting according to rule and tides flowing and ebbing systematically for man's convenience, is, after all, a thing of mystery. It is a vast darkness in that its heart is inscrutable. What, then, has Marlow gained, since he has ended with this conclusion which we might, *a priori,* accept as a platitude? He has certainly helped us eliminate the false assumptions by which day to day we act as if the universe were a very simple contrivance, even while, perhaps, we give lip service[159] to the contrary. Moreover, instead of letting one faculty of the mind dominate and deny the pertinence of the others, he has achieved a reconciliation in which physical sensation, imagination, and that conscious logic which selects and arranges have lost their apparent qualities of contradiction. He has achieved an orderly explanation, conscious and methodical, of the strange purlieus of the imagination. Because those recesses harbor shadows, the exploration must not be labeled conclusive; but the greatness of the darkness, instead of leaving a sense of the futility of efforts to dispel it, has drawn the artist to use his utmost conscious skill. Life itself, if we agree with Conrad, may tend to seem to us as meaningless and chaotic as were many of Marlow's sensations at the moment of his undergoing them, and the will may often appear to play no part at all, or a false part, in guiding us. But the genius of art was for Conrad that it accepted the most intense and seemingly reason-defying creations of the imagination and then discovered within them, rather than superimposed upon them, a symmetry coherent and logical.

Through Marlow's orderly narrative, with its perfect identity of fact and symbol, with its transformation of time and space into emotional and imaginative intensity, the shadows have contracted, and we are better able than before to speculate on the presences which seem to inhabit the very heart of darkness. Time is telescoped and we have as if in the same moment the exalted enthusiast and the man who denied all except horror; and we realize that they are and always have been the same man. We perceive that Africa itself, with its forests, its heat, and its mysteries, is only a symbol of the larger darkness, which is in the heart of man.[160]

THE LIE AND TRUTH*

Thomas C. Moser

Finishing Part III of "The Rescuer" in December, 1898, Conrad soon abandoned Part IV to write "Heart of Darkness," which was published in *Youth and Two Other Stories,* 1902. As in "Youth," all the principal characters are male. But Marlow, the narrator, makes some interesting comments on women; the last scene, between Marlow and Kurtz's Intended has considerable significance; and the jungle imagery raises some interesting problems. Marlow's most extended comment on women comes out apropos of his aunt's expostulations on the great missionary work of the Congo trading company. Marlow ventures to remind her that the company is run for profit, and then says in an aside to his male audience on board the yawl in the Thames estuary:

> It's queer how out of touch with truth women are. They live in a world of their own, and there has never been anything like it, and never can be. It is too beautiful altogether, and if they were to set it up it would go to pieces before the first sunset. Some confounded fact we men have been living contentedly with ever since the day of creation would start up and knock the whole thing over.[78]

In the context of "Heart of Darkness," with its theme of self-discovery, Marlow's assertion that women can take no part in the quest for truth is severe criticism indeed. Marlow says the same thing of Kurtz's Intended: "Oh, she is out of it—completely. They—the women I mean—are out of it—should be out of it. We must help them to stay in that beautiful world of their own."

Though "Heart of Darkness" does not hint that Marlow has any sexual interest in the Intended, their scene together at the end certainly recalls in some respects scenes between the Herveys in "The Return." For instance, though Marlow has been eager to meet her, he is filled with horror when he reaches her door. The fireplace in her drawing room has a "cold and monumental whiteness." Marlow looks at the woman and wonders what he is doing there, "with a sensation

* Reprinted by permission of the publisher from Thomas C. Moser, *Joseph Conrad: Achievement and Decline,* Cambridge, Mass.: Harvard University Press, Copyright 1957, by the President and Fellows of Harvard College. [Title mine. Ed.]

of panic in my heart as though I had blundered into a place of cruel and absurd mysteries not fit for a human being to behold." Their ensuing dialogue is halting and wooden, a "bad patch" of prose, F. R. Leavis calls it.[1] Marlow has come there hoping to surrender to her the memory of Kurtz. She instead maneuvers him into telling her a lie: that Kurtz's last words were, not "The horror," but her name: "I heard a light sigh and then my heart stood still, stopped dead short by an exulting and terrible cry, by the cry of inconceivable triumph and of unspeakable pain." Marlow's lie certainly weakens the scene; he has made truth seem too important throughout the novel to persuade the reader now to accept falsehood as salvation.

The extended descriptions of the jungle remind us, not unnaturally, of the vegetation imagery of *Almayer's Folly* and *An Outcast of the Islands*. Here, too, the "vegetation rioted on the earth and the big trees were kings"; the reader finds himself in a "strange world of plants, water, and silence." Yet "Heart of Darkness" does not stress so heavily as the earlier works the strangling effects of tendrils and creepers.[79] At one point, Marlow does mention the "living trees, lashed together by the creepers," and at another he equates vegetation with woman just as he does not only in the Malay stories but also in *The Sisters*. The jungle woman is, of course, Kurtz's native mistress, "savage and superb, wild-eyed and magnificent." Marlow comments:

> And in the hush that had fallen suddenly upon the whole sorrowful land, the immense wilderness, the colossal body of the fecund and mysterious life seemed to look at her, pensive, as though it had been looking at the image of its own tenebrous and passionate soul.

Any reader of "Heart of Darkness" must recognize that our analysis of it in terms of sexual love hardly scratches the surface. It means far more than this, and herein lies its significance. For the first time Conrad has been able to use material potentially related to sex in such a way as not to ruin his story and, in fact, in some respects to strengthen it. Our account of the imagery of the Congo jungle far from exhausts its meanings; rather, this imagery has the richness and tonality of the true symbol. The jungle stands for "truth," for an "amazing reality." Conrad equates it with the African natives who alone are full of vitality; the whites are but hollow men. Yet the jungle also means the "lurking death," "profound darkness," and "evil," which belong to the prehistoric life of man, our heritage. We cannot escape this heritage; going into the jungle seems to Marlow like traveling into one's own past, into the world of one's dreams, into the subconscious. Thus the vegetation imagery means much more than female menace; it means the truth, the darkness, the evil, the death which lie within us, which we must recognize in order to be truly

---

1 F. R. Leavis, *The Great Tradition* (London, 1948), p. 181.

alive. In the same way, while the scene between Marlow and Kurtz's Intended is imperfect, and while it does show the "inconceivable triumph" of woman over man, it has other, more important functions in the story. The scene can be read, for example, as an indictment of this[80] woman, safe and ignorant in her complacent, Belgian bourgeois existence; she does not *deserve* to hear the truth. The scene can also be read as Marlow's reaffirmation of fellowship with Kurtz. To accept Kurtz's pronouncement, "The horror," means accepting damnation; Marlow's sin, the lie, serves to confirm this.[81]

THE LIGHT AND DARK LIE*

Wilfred S. Dowden

Marlow's task was not over, however [after the death of Kurtz]. There was still Kurtz's "intended" to see—to face with the burden of the knowledge of Kurtz's extreme degradation. She, too, was a shadowy figure, dressed in black, seen in the dusk. As Marlow spoke to her the room darkened and "only her forehead, smooth and white, remained illumined by the unextinguishable light of belief and love." Like everything else associated with the man, she was a dim, almost spectral figure. As Marlow listened to her she became, like Kurtz, only a voice, which "seemed to have the accompaniment of all the other sounds, full of mystery, desolation, and sorrow ... the whisper of a voice speaking from beyond the threshold of an eternal darkness" (pp. 67-68).

This girl had been anticipated by the tragic figure of the native woman who stretched her bare arms over the water toward the departing steamer, just as the emaciated Kurtz had been prefigured by the dying natives in the deep, dim shade of the company station. The girl, like the native woman, "put out her arms as if after a retreating figure, stretching them black and with clasped pale hands across the fading and narrow sheen of the window" (p. 68). The girl and the native woman are kindred spirits, because each had lost the man who, in the darkness of his existence in the[48] heart of the Dark Continent, could not trust or be trusted by any other human being.

---

* Quoted by permission of the Rice Institute from "The Light and the Dark; Imagery and Thematic Development in Conrad's *Heart of Darkness*," *Rice Institute Pamphlet*, XLIV (April, 1957), 33-51. [Title mine. Ed.]

In the end Marlow could not tell this woman the truth about Kurtz. His last words, said Marlow, were the young woman's name. To tell her what he had actually said "would have been too dark—too dark altogether," would have opened the bleakness of his heart to her view; and she would have known the depths to which he had sunk.

She would also have seen something more sinister, for she would have seen that which Kurtz had perceived even before he reached the debased state in which Marlowe found him. Kurtz had expressed his perception in a painting which he had left at one of the stations before he went into the heart of the Dark Continent. This painting was a "sketch in oils, on a panel, representing a woman, draped and blindfolded, carrying a lighted torch. The background was somber—almost black. The movement of the woman was stately, and the effect of the torchlight on the face was sinister." (p. 21) Significantly, Marlow saw this painting in the light of a single candle. The sketch only increased the mystery of Kurtz at the time, and prompted Marlow to make further inquiries about the agent. When the darkness surrounding Kurtz is partially dispelled, however, the reader (and perhaps Marlow) sees what Kurtz intended the painting to mean; it symbolizes mankind, groping blindly through the darkness of his existence, seeking his way with what light civilization can offer. But this light also emphasizes the somber, sinister nature of man, just as the fierce sunlight beating down on the starving native, as he crept from the shade of the trees, emphasized his abased state. In a sense it betrays man, as it had betrayed the white clerk, who had mistakenly identified its superficial, dazzling whiteness with reality. To Kurtz,[49] however, the light illuminated that which is most sinister in the heart of man; it enabled him to see through the mask and perceive, perhaps too clearly, how thin the surface layer of civilization really is. Kurtz knew of the blackness, the darkness which is at the heart of humanity; he knew the depths to which man is capable of sinking; he knew that the light of civilization could not penetrate this darkness, could only emphasize its sinister pervasiveness; and worst of all, he knew that he had turned away from this feeble light, so that he had been enveloped in the darkness which is at the heart of every man. He had, in the end, "pronounced a judgment upon the adventures of his soul on this earth." Kurtz was a remarkable man because he had perceived this darkness, and since Marlow had vicariously partaken of Kurtz's revelation, he was the only person associated with the agent who could come near to penetrating the meaning of Kurtz's summing up: "The horror! the horror!" He could understand the meaning of Kurtz's stare as the man lay dying—a stare "that could not see the flame of the candle, but was wide enough to embrace the whole universe, piercing enough to penetrate all the hearts that beat in the darkness" (p. 63). To explain all this to Kurtz's fiancée would have been "too dark—too dark altogether." Only he who has "peeped over the edge" himself can understand it in all its horror.

Marlow finished his tale, and a silence fell upon the group of men on the ship. Perhaps they had also "peeped over the edge" and had learned something of the revelation which came so forcibly to Kurtz. This fact seems to be implied in Conrad's conclusion to *The Heart of Darkness,* in which he focuses the reader's attention again on these friends who heard Marlow's tale, thus completing the framework to his narrative. As they gazed westward they were conscious that[50] "the offing was barred by a black bank of clouds, and the tranquil waterway leading to the uttermost ends of the earth flowed sombre under an overcast sky—seemed to lead into the heart of an immense darkness" (p. 69).[51]

TEXTUAL NOTE

Contrary to the general impression, the status of Conrad's texts is by no means clear. The notes which follow apply only to "Heart of Darkness," though presumably other works of Conrad follow the same pattern.

Previous editors of Conrad have followed the lead of Richard Curle, Conrad's friend, who said that though many forms of the fiction exist, Conrad concerned himself with only one—"the collected edition book form." (*The Last Twelve Years of Joseph Conrad*. p. 64.) But which collected edition? General practice has been to print from the Dent (English) or perhaps the Doubleday (American) general collected editions. The present edition is the first of any of Conrad's works to be based on a full collation of all important texts. These are as follows (in book form, of course, in the *Youth* volume):

B. Serial version. "The Heart of Darkness." Published in *Blackwood's Edinburgh Magazine* in three instalments: Feb., 1899 (pp. 193-220); March, 1899 (pp. 479-502); April, 1899 (pp. 634-657). These correspond to the parts as published in book form. Hereafter referred to as *B*.

E. First English edition. Blackwood's, 1902. Hereafter referred to as *E*.

A. First American edition. McClure, Phillips, 1903. Hereafter referred to as *A*. (Contrary to Conrad's note in the Curle collection volume, closer to *E* than to *B* in its text.)

AD. Doubleday (American) edition, 1910. (From the same plates as *A*, but with slight variants; presumably the same as the 1903 Doubleday, as yet not found by the editor.) Hereafter referred to as *AD*.

CS. Collected, limited American edition, "Sun-Dial," beginning in 1920. Hereafter referred to as *CS*.

CD. Collected, general American "edition," "Kent." This like the "Malay," and others, was issued by Doubleday after the middle 'Twenties. (Same plates as *CS*, but with slight variation.) Hereafter referred to as *CD*.

CU. Collected, general English "edition," the Dent "Uniform," beginning in 1923. This is made from duplicate plates of *CS* and is identical with it after the title page; it is not a separate setting of type. Not an edition in the strict sense. (The current Dent Collected, 1946–, is from the same plates.) This is the generally accepted copy-text, though faulty in detail. Hereafter referred to as *CU*.

CH. Collected, limited English edition, by Heinemann, beginning in 1921. (This is the copy-text for the present edition.) Hereafter referred to as *CH*.

D. The Dent *Youth* volume of 1917, for which Conrad wrote the Author's Note. Hereafter referred to as *D.*

MS. The manuscript has not been collated, but has been read against *CH* to help settle various readings.

Preparation of the present text has led to several conclusions, though they must be treated as tentative until more of Conrad's letters are published, or until publishers' files may be consulted. *CH* is taken as copy-text for many reasons which have a cumulative effect, though no one is conclusive; here reprinted for the first time.

1. *CS* was done in a foreign country, and perhaps the author did not revise fully for it.

2. *CU* (and the current Dent collected edition) is made from the Sun-Dial plates. Though Dent speaks of the text as "authorized and final," the very nature of the reprinting would preclude major changes.

3. It follows that *CH* was the last separate printing of Conrad's complete work in his lifetime, and may therefore be the edition he spoke about to Curle.

4. There is the negative evidence that Conrad's published letters nowhere speak of revising for *CU.* On the contrary, his letter of 3 Sept., 1920 (*Life and Letters,* II, 247-248) to the Heinemann firm, shows very careful editing on the part of the firm and Conrad, for the *CH Nigger.* Perhaps like care went into the preparation of the other novels and tales.

5. A study of the *MS* shows that even in accidentals—spelling, punctuation, capitals, and the like—*CH* is closer to Conrad than any other edition, even *A* and *E.* This unusual situation has led me to follow *CH* in accidentals except when clearly contradicted by the *MS.* Space forbids much illustration of variation in accidentals among the texts, but a remark on spelling might be made: words such as "honour" are given the English spelling in *CS* and *CD,* but less obvious ones ("authorize" for "authorise") retain the American form—perhaps indicating a text prepared in America, but intended to be distributed in England as well.

One illustration of variations in substantives must suffice. Consider p. 31, where the reading is ". . . inborn strength. Principles? Principles won't do." in *CH, A, AD, E, B, D, MS* (varies); but where the rhetorical question is left out in *CS, CD, CU,* presumably by a typesetter. This indicates that after *CS* the publisher did not check his text against earlier editions. Of the late editions, only *CH* is correct.

Perhaps some evidence should here be given for the assertion that *CU, CD,* and the current Dent Collected, are all from *CS* plates. Page 113 of that edition must suffice. The phrase "at the shoe-laces," if examined closely, will be found to have a heavily inked "at," and to be out of parallel with the rest of the line. Indeed, it would appear that from this point on the whole type-face shifted slightly—a clear indication that all four are printed from the same plates, or rather from plates made from one parent. Broken type, indeed, can be traced through the four "editions," and a close examination of virtually any page will reveal duplicate plates.

It is greatly regretted that the collations cannot be given in full. The notes that follow, because of limited space, are but examples of the variations in the text. I have been most concerned to show (1) when I have emended the copy-text, and (2) when *CU* and *CD* have gone astray. Other editions, such as the Modern Library paperback, of course have no authority and have not been collated.

The student may ask why changes from early editions are not to be looked upon as authorial corrections. Some are clearly errors, brought about either by slips on the part of type-setters, or by the tamperings of publishers' editors who thought they were improving the text. One cannot always be sure, of course, but the deletion of "Principles?" as cited above is an example of one kind of error; the substitution of "boat" in *CS, CU, CD* for "float" p. 33 above is an example of the other kind. (See *O.E.D.* for the meaning of "float.")

Lest it seem unlikely that a publisher would make such changes, consider an obvious one. The Signet edition of "Heart of Darkness" changes Marlow's use of the word "verily" to "truly" throughout the tale. Lest the other class of change seem insignificant, consider the Signet edition's reading in the scene in which the intimacy of Marlow and Kurtz is being founded. Marlow says that Kurtz's soul had looked within itself, and that he himself had, for his sins, "to go through the ordeal of looking into myself." So the Signet edition, pp. 129-130. On page 59 above, the correct reading will be found: "to go through the ordeal of looking into it [Kurtz's soul] myself." The difference is of one word, but a crucial one, in a crucial passage. The passage might be made the basis for an interpretation of the story, and the reader of the Signet edition would be led very much astray.

The notes that follow indicate most of the substantive variations within the important editions in book form, though they tend to stress departures from *CD* and *CU* rather than from *A* and *E*. There seems little point in trying to record the fact that Conrad made many, many revisions after *MS, B,* and even *E* and *A*. Accidentals are listed in a separate table, followed by another which shows a few of the changes from *MS* to *B*. The word *"all"* is used to indicate that all editions other than those specified have the same reading. The numeral following the decimal point indicates the line on the page, and all page references are to the present text. The asterisk indicates a departure from the copy-text, *CH*.

Substantive and Semi-substantive Variants

Page Line			
	(Epigraph; appears first in book form):		
[xi]	of all the world *all*	of the world *CU*	
1.10	sprits. *all* [*MS* missing]	spirits. *CS, CU*	
2.24	has borne *CH*	had borne *all* [*MS* missing]	
11.7	six-inch *AD, CD, CH, CS, CU, D*	eight-inch *all*	ten-inch *MS*

12.37	from the sea. *AD, CD, CH, CS, CU, D*	from over the sea. *all*
13.30	The rapids *all*	The river *B, MS*
14.2*	of the eyes *AD, CD, CH, CS, CU, D*	of eyes *all*
14.30*	clear necktie *all*	clean necktie *AD, CD, CH*
	a clear [*clear* is added above the line, difficult to read] silk necktie *MS*	
14.46	later, I *CD, CH, CS, CU, D*	later on, I *all* [*MS* has no comma]
15.20	invalided *all*	invalid *CD, CS, CU*
17.10	remembered . . . doctor—'It *CD, CH*	remember . . . doctor,—'It *CS, CU* remembered . . . doctor,—'It *all*
	remembered . . . doctor "it *MS*	
19.11	'How can I *CD, CH*	'How could I *all* "How . . . *MS*
19.11	'I haven't *CD, CH*	'I hadn't *all* "I hadn't *MS*
19.33*	those months! *CH*	these months! *all*
20.3	, later, for *CD, CH, CS, CU, D*	, later on, for *all*
	later on for *MS*	
20.26	Anyway, *CH*	Anyways, *all* [*MS* has no comma]
21.10	full only of chills, *CD, CH, CS, CU, D*	full of chills, *all* [*MS* has no comma]
21.18	an empty half-pint *CD, CH, CS, CU, D*	a half-pint *all*
21.19	champagne bottle *all*	bottle of champagne *B, MS*
26.16	like the spoils *all*	like spoils *CS, CU*
27.35	As for me *CH*	As to me *all*
28.16	possible.' *all*	best.' *CD, CS, CU*
	possible." *MS*	
30.44	on a prehistoric *all*	on prehistoric *CS, CU*
31.34	strength. Principles? Principles won't *all*	strength. Principles won't *CD, CS, CU*
	hide everything. Principles? Principles—acquisitions, *MS*	
33.33	float, *all* [*MS* has no comma]	boat, *CD, CS, CU*
35.11	will all be butchered *CH*	will be all butchered *all*
36.14	look of *CH*	looks of *all*
45.46	revenged. *all*	avenged. *CD, CS, CU*
46.41	binding round *all*	binding around *CD, CS, CU*
47.39	I met *CD, CH, CS, CU, D*	I have met *all*
48.5	I sent *CH, MS*	I've sent *all*
50.42*	there were the *CH*	there was the *all*
51.8*	for vultures *CD, CH*	for the vultures *all*
52.6	to him that Mr. *AD, CD, CH, CS, CU, D*	to him Mr. *all* [period varies]

52.25*	forests *CH*	forest *all*
58.25*	within thirty yards from *all*	within thirty yards of *MS*
65.31	those ironic *CD, CH*	these ironic *all*
67.10	quickly out *CD, CH, CS, CU*	quick out *all*
68.1	of the crowds, *CD, CH, CS, CU, D*	of wild crowds, *all*
68.36*	back *CH*	black *all*

Accidentals

One can even say that the restoration of Conrad's punctuation is of equal importance to the substantive corrections. I have made no effort to record purely formal variations in the book—the use of ornamental devices, long dashes rather than short ones, etc. *CD, CS,* and *CU* in general follow the early editions, but tend to point far more heavily. For example, there are very many commas added, especially before adverbs; and the use of the comma and dash together (not used in *MS* and *CH*) is even increased in *CD, CS,* and *CU*. It is regretted that only a few of the hundreds of variations among these texts can be recorded here. Meaning is not changed by these practices, yet the heavy pointing throughout *CD, CS, CU* has a definite effect on the texture of the story. Although I have given examples of items where I depart from the copy-text, the following sample variations show that in nearly all cases *CH* and *MS* agree.

Page Line			
xiii.10	*Youth* *CH, D*	"Youth" *CD, CS, CU*	
4.12	him— *CH*	him,— *all*	him, *MS*
4.16	abomination—you know. Imagine *all* [*MS* missing]	abomination—you know, imagine *CD, CS, CU*	abomination—you know, Imagine *D*
8.30	vermuths *all*	vermouths *A, AD*	
8.39	callipers *CH, MS*	calipers *all*	
9.8	original imperturbably. *CH, MS*	original, imperturbably. *all*	
11.27	particularised *B, CH, D, E*	particularized *all*	
13.35	trees, leaning *all*	trees leaning *CD, CS, CU*	
13.42	now—nothing *CH*	now nothing *MS*	now,—nothing *all*
14.32*	penholder *all*	pen-holder *CH*	
14.43	demoralisation *all*	demoralization *A, AD, CD, CS, CU*	
16.28*	sleep, strike *all*	sleep; strike *CH*	
16.44*	coming-to. *all*	coming to. *CH*	
16.46	said scornfully. *CH, MS*	said, scornfully. *all*	
20.15	by and by *CD, CH*	by-and-by *all*	by and bye *MS*
20.40	account—but *CH, MS*	account,—but *all*	
20.41*	heavens! *all*	Heavens! *CH*	heavens. *MS*
21.28	entrusted *CH, MS*	intrusted *all*	

22.9*	'Heap *all*	"Heap *B, MS*	'Heaps *CH*
23.27	existence— *CD, CH, CS, CU, D, MS*	existence,— *all*	
25.5	work—the *CH, MS*	work,—the *all*	
30.22	'ivory' *CH*	ivory *all*	
32.31	Hurry up. Where? *all*	'Hurry up.' Where? *CD*	Hurry up! *MS*
32.46	Towser, Towson *CD, CH*	Tower, Towson *all*	
	[Not clear in *MS* Towzer(?), Towson]		
36.45	chaps too had *all*	chaps, too, had *CD, CS, CU*	
37.19	other—and *CH, MS*	other, and *all*	
53.8*	—Kurtz— *all*	—Kirtz— *CH*	
56.3	He suspected 'there *CH*	'He suspected there *all*	
	He suspected there *B*		
	[*MS* usage of quotation marks is confusing here, as in many other sections.]		
56.38	etc. etc. *CH*	etc etc *MS*	
	etc., etc. *CD, CS, CU, D*	&c., &c. *all*	
56.40	own too it *all*	own, too, it *CD, CS, CU*	
61.13	mould *all* [*MS* missing]	mold *A, AD*	
67.14	said unsteadily. *CH, MS*	said, unsteadily. *all*	
69.18	horror! The horror!' *CH*	"Oh! the horror!" *MS*	
	horror! the horror!' *all*		
69.35	Director suddenly. *CH, MS*	Director, suddenly. *all*	

Manuscript and Serial

The study of an author's revisions from manuscript through serial to book form is an illuminating experience, but is not within the aim of this book. The following notes are intended in no way to offer more than the merest flavor of the manuscript. Interested students may turn to the Gordan and Keating volumes. (See Bibliography.) In general, it can be said that up to page 52 of the present edition, the serial and the manuscript agree fairly closely with later texts—though a few pages of the *MS* are missing, and Conrad cut a few more pages from it before it went to the serial form. Differences of a few words, or a few sentences are fairly common in *MS* and *B*, but after page 52, wording varies two or three times to a page.

Limitations of space prevent giving many examples, but seven typical kinds of changes follow, showing variation among *B, CH,* and *MS* only.* It might be added that the *MS* shows no clear indication of chapter breaks in the story. (Italicized words in the notes indicate after-thought additions in the *MS;* words in square brackets are those deleted by Conrad.)

* My thanks are due to Yale University Library, which holds the *MS,* for supplying a film of the *MS* and giving permission to publish therefrom; thanks are also due J. M. Dent and Sons, Ltd., and Blackwood (William) & Sons, Ltd., for permission to quote from the *MS* and the serial.

Page Line

no doubt [Monsieur] *meet* Mr [Klein] *Kurtz*." *MS*
15.26 no doubt meet Mr. Kurtz.' *CH* [and *B*, except for accidentals.]

soul. ¶ "And we men also looked at her—at any rate I looked at her. She *B, MS* [except . . . her; at . . .]
54.20 soul. ¶ "She *CH*

she stopped. Had her heart failed her, or had her eyes veiled with that mournfulness that lies over all the wild things *of the earth* seen the hopelessness of longing that will find out *sometimes* even a savage soul in the loneliness of its being? Who can tell. Perhaps she did not know herself. The young fellow *MS*
she . . . eyes, veiled . . . the lonely darkness . . . fellow *B*
54.28 she stopped as if her heart had failed her. The young fellow *CH*

though she had tried to touch the sky and the shadows of her arms darted out *on the earth* swept around *on the river* as if gathering the steamer into a shadowy embrace. *MS*
. . . sky, and at the same time the shadows of her arms darted out on the earth, swept around on the river, gathering . . . *B*
. . . sky, and at the same time the swift shadows darted out . . .
54.33 *CH* [as *B*]

looking into *it* myself. No eloquence could be so withering as *his final* [his] *burst of* sincerity. *MS*
looking . . . could have been so withering . . . *B* [as *MS*]
59.31 looking . . . withering to one's belief in mankind as . . . *CH* [as *MS*]

simplicity "I have lived—supremely."—"I have been dead—and damned"—Let me go—I want more of it." More of what? More blood, more heads on staves <stakes? *MS* film not clear>, more adoration rapine and murder. I remembered *MS*
simplicity: 'I have lived—supremely!' 'What do you want here? I have been dead . . . *B* [as *MS*, except for accidentals and *stakes*.]
66.7 simplicity. I remembered *CH*

—Yes I know I said *with something like despair in my heart but* bowing my head before the faith that was in her, before that great and saving illusion which shone with an unearthly glow in the darkness, in the triumphant darkness [that enveloped us both and all <all? *MS* film not clear>] *from* which I could not [experience <? *MS* film not clear> alone] have defended her—from which I could not *even* defend myself. *MS*
68.5 " 'Yes, I know . . . myself. [*B, CH* as corrected *MS*, except for accidentals and *which shone* <that shone>.]

In sum, then, it can be said that *CH* is a very good copy-text. I have followed it in almost all substantive readings, and for some of the readings I have rejected (for example, see the note above to p. 51.8 "for vultures"), *CH* certainly can also be defended.

In accidentals I have also followed *CH* in nearly all variants. The ideal copy-text, one supposes, for "Heart of Darkness" so far as accidentals are concerned would be the corrected typescript (apparently done in the Blackwood office for the most part) which went to the printers. That form of the story has not survived. I have often not followed the *MS* in accidentals for two reasons: (1) Conrad was an indefatigable reviser of his texts, and (2) the *MS* is clearly wrong in matters such as we might expect an author in the throes of composition to ignore. (The *MS* often mismanages single and double quotation marks, for example.) Furthermore, *CH* has the unusual value of being pointed according to the same philosophy of style as is the *MS*. That is, it is "open," or "light" pointing. The heavy-handed pointing we think of as Conrad's seems to have had its source in the practice of Blackwood, Dent, and Doubleday, not in the author's. (Studies of *TSS* other than "Heart of Darkness" tend to support this conclusion. See, for example, G. W. Whiting, "Conrad's Revision of 'The Lighthouse' in *Nostromo*," *PMLA*, LII [December, 1937].) The comparative rarity of copies of *CH* (780 were made before the type was distributed) has caused the critics' estimate of the style of "Heart of Darkness" to be set, erroneously, by *CD* and *CU*.

Of the editions in general, this may be added. The proper line of descent is *MS*, [*TS*,] *B*, *E*, through the English editions to *D*, which apparently served as copy-text for *CH*. That last conclusion is not only supported by the dates of the editions, but by the agreement in accidentals in the "Author's Note." As the above Textual Note indicates, *CH* is the best edition hitherto available, while *CD*, rather oddly, is the second best. It makes certain proper corrections over *CS* and *CU*, though unfortunately and strangely, many of them are no more important than the removal of hyphens in the phrase "by-and-by." (See note to p. 20.15.)

Finally, it should be said that the present edition is not intended as a definitive edition—for example, there is no space for full collation notes, there are no explanatory notes, there are no emendations although some are certainly called for, and copy-text has even been silently departed from a few times. I have been conservative in that last matter, for odd readings such as "secular trees" (p. 61), having the support of all editions and the *MS*, give one pause. *Conrad's "Heart of Darkness" and the Critics*, then, presents simply a good reading edition for study.

STUDY QUESTIONS, THEME AND PAPER TOPICS

"Heart of Darkness" is so rich a story that a wealth of issues of all sorts is raised by it, even after one has read a selection of the best criticism. The questions which follow are in no way exhaustive, nor are they intended to direct the student or the teacher into a particular approach to the tale. Rather, they are sample questions which the instructor will likely modify. Their organization is especially flexible, and questions intended by the editor as term paper topics might well be used for themes, or for essay questions on examinations.

Study Questions

1. Characterize the manager.
2. Try to account for all the characters and details of the story which strike you as odd, outstanding, catching. For example, what purpose is served by including the accountant in the story? the brickmaker? the barbarian woman at Kurtz's station? What is the function of the knitting women in the city in Europe? of the Pilgrims with their staves? Contrast Marlow's fireman with his helmsman. Compare the scene of the helmsman's death with Kurtz's. Have the critics "solved" all these questions for you? Notice, for example, Albert Guerard's suggestion that there are many possible meanings to Marlow's throwing his bloody shoes overboard. Does Conrad control these meanings? Remember that Marlow steps into Fresleven's shoes (p. 6), that he tugs at his shoe-laces (p. 41), that he gives the Russian a pair of shoes (p. 56), and that the packet of letters destined for the Intended is tied with a shoe-string (p. 61).
3. Observe Conrad's use of color, particularly of black and white. We usually associate black with evil, white with good; how far has Conrad simply reversed this? Note for example the tone in which the "whited sepulchre" is spoken of.
4. Notice Conrad's frequent use of the demonstrative adjective where one might ordinarily use an article: *that* river, *that* steamboat, *these* Pilgrims, and so on. What is the effect of this usage?
5. Look up the term *irony*. Can you classify kinds of irony in the story? How much of the story turns on irony of language—ways of expressing things, as contrasted to, say, ironic situations or characters or conflicts?

6. Why did Kurtz, do you think, go back up-river, after once having started down with ivory?
7. Why are we told that Kurtz is a "universal genius"? Or that "all Europe contributed to the making of Kurtz"? In this line of thought, what is the effect of Marlow's various interviews with the organist, the journalist, etc., after he has returned to Europe?
8. Why doesn't Marlow turn savage, as Kurtz had done? Specifically, why doesn't he go ashore for a howl and a dance? (See p. 31.)
9. When Marlow is talking to the Manager, he says he turned to Kurtz "for relief" (p. 55). What is meant? How does the phrase, "unsound method," apply here? Why, a few lines later, does Marlow correct himself, saying that he had turned to the wilderness really, not to Kurtz? What is the meaning of the wilderness in this story?
10. Trace Marlow's interest in Kurtz, step by step, beginning with an idle curiosity, through Marlow's feeling that the voyage was exclusively to Kurtz, to Marlow's identifying himself with Kurtz and feeling that "it is his extremity that I seem to have lived through" (p. 63).
11. How does Conrad manage the transitions between the inner story and the outer framework?
12. How would you characterize the effect of the story? Conrad, in his letters to his publisher, Blackwood (see Bibliography), often likened "Heart of Darkness" to "Youth," although he would imply that its effect was not that of the "nostalgia" of "Youth." [See also the "Author's Note," p. xiv, above.] Still, the "narrative is not gloomy," he added, though he allowed it had an "African nightmare" quality. Can you sum up its effect?

Theme Topics

1. Using the Textual Note in this volume, can you catalogue the kinds of changes made in the text through the years? Do the variant readings listed in that Note help your understanding of the story, or Conrad as an artist, to any great extent?
2. "Heart of Darkness" is in part autobiographical. Contrast "The Congo Diary," which, of course, is strictly autobiographical. Write an essay around the vast differences in mood, tone, purpose, effect.
3. How far does the biographical section of this book help you understand "Heart of Darkness"—as distinct from helping you understand Conrad as a man?
4. Discuss the atmosphere or mood of the story as it relates to its meaning. Be sure to treat these points: the dreamlike or nightmare element, on which Marlow insists frequently: and the statement by the final narrator that for Marlow the meaning of a yarn was "not inside like a kernel but outside, enveloping the tale which brought it out only as a glow brings out a haze. . . ." See Conrad's remark on "resonance" in the "Author's Note," p. xiv, above.

5. Marlow tells "Heart of Darkness" virtually in the order in which its events happened to him. At one point (pp. 42 to 45), however, he jumps ahead in time. For that brief passage, he gives us later events, those roughly of the period of time covered on page 61. Why? What effect does this "violation" of chronological order have?
6. How would you characterize Marlow's language (not Conrad's)? Discuss not only his love of irony, but the quality of his style. Notice his use of Biblical allusion, of the word "verily," of half-hidden proverbs, such as the one about stealing a horse (p. 20).
7. Is the ending, in fact, adjectival, as so many critics assert?
8. How much of the meaning of the story is contained in the phrase "the fascination of the abomination" (p. 4)?
9. Have the critics made absolutely clear to you why Kurtz's final cry, "The horror! The horror!" is both a victory and an affirmation? What is defeated? What is being affirmed? What stress should be put on Marlow's statement that "the shade of the original Kurtz frequented the bedside of the hollow sham" (p. 61)?
10. Marlow says (p. 29) that when you have to turn your attention to work, you are looking to "mere incidents of the surface, [and] the reality—the reality, I tell you—fades. The inner truth is hidden —luckily, luckily." But later he adds (p. 31) that in the work there was "surface-truth enough . . . to save a wiser man." At an earlier point, further, he had expressed himself more firmly on the subject of work: "I don't like work—no man does—but I like what is in the work—the chance to find yourself. Your own reality —for yourself, not for others—what no other man can ever know" (p. 25).

    Does Conrad seem to be setting up two kinds or qualities of reality? How can you reconcile these statements?
11. Consider Marlow's Lie at the end of the story. Does the notion of two kinds of reality apply here? Can that idea be used to amplify what the various critics say on the subject? Conrad, it should be remembered, was rather proud of that ending. "The last pages of Heart of Darkness where the interview of the man and the girl locks in—as it were—the whole 30000 words of narrative description into one suggestive view of a whole phase of life, . . . makes of that story something quite on another plane than an anecdote of a man who went mad in the Centre of Africa." (Joseph Conrad, *Letters to William Blackwood,* p. 154.)

    What stress should be put on Marlow's words (p. 42) that he "laid the ghost of his [Kurtz's] gifts at last with a lie"?

    Can you compare the Lie with the end of Conrad's "The Secret Sharer" where the Captain endangers his ship by sailing too close to Koh-ring?
12. How far is the meaning of the story concerned with the evil of man in his essential nature? How far is it a story about the disease of modern, social man, at a particular point in history?

Longer Essays and Term Papers

1. Write a history of the Belgian colonies in the Congo. Is Conrad true to historical fact in his picture? To what extent have things changed in central Africa since Conrad's time? To what extent is the political situation of our times the result of such things as Conrad saw in the 1890's?
2. Contrast Kurtz with Albert Schweitzer.
3. Working first with the books listed in the Bibliography, especially those by Jerry Allen, Jocelyn Baines, J. D. Gordan, and the letters of Conrad to Marguerite Poradowska, construct your own interpretive biography of Conrad at the time of his Congo adventure. Can his statement, reported by several critics, that he was a "mere animal" before he went to Africa be taken as your central thesis? Contrast "The Congo Diary" with Conrad as you now know him.
4. Read Conrad's letters to William Blackwood (See Bibliography), especially the sections dealing with "Heart of Darkness" and the *Youth* volume. Does an understanding of the troubles and achievements of Conrad the man, during the period of writing and publishing the story, add to your enjoyment of it? How important would you say his publisher was to him? Was Blackwood only a "businessman"? Can you infer anything from the letters about the structure of the story? What, for example, seems to have governed the chapter divisions of the finished tale?
5. At least one school of criticism holds that one should begin by annotation of the work of art. Write footnotes explaining the meaning of the following details: *Erebus* and *Terror* (p. 2), Fleet Street (p. 5), Deal and Gravesend (p. 16), Zanzibaris (p. 16), the Chapman lighthouse (p. 2). Can you find the source of the epigraph of the book? Does its context help you understand the story? Annotate the phrases "whited sepulchre," "swept and ungarnished" (p. 7). You will find many other details and allusions which should be annotated. For example, A. M. Hollingsworth in *Literature and Psychology* (November, 1955) has suggested that in the Pilgrims' staves is an allusion to the Bible. Christ specifically warned his "lower Apostles" not to carry staves (Luke 9.3).
6. Discuss the unity of the *Youth* volume. Remember that Conrad originally intended the volume to consist of "Youth," "Heart of Darkness," and "Lord Jim." He felt that "the three tales, each being inspired by a similar moral idea (or is it only one of my optical delusions?) will make (in that sense) a homogenous book" (Blackwood letters, p. 79). Does the epigraph of the book help you understand its unity? In one of her books, Mrs. Conrad testifies that Conrad, in response to her puzzled question, said that the epigraph applied to the dedication only. Might he have told her less than the truth? Might he have been himself unconscious of some of the meaning of the epigraph? On the unity of the volume, one must also remember that Conrad later wrote F. N. Doubleday

(*Life and Letters,* II, 338; letter of Feb. 7, 1924) that the volume as eventually published was unified: "the volume of *Youth,* which in its component parts presents the three ages of man (for that is what it really is, and I knew very well what I was doing when I wrote 'The End of the Tether' to be the last of that trio). . . ." Contrast the opening sentence to the "Author's Note" of the *Youth* volume, which Conrad wrote in 1917.

7. Notice that Kurtz (and Marlow at one point, but that is a different issue) is characterized as "a voice." Remember also that one man whom Marlow interviews at the end says that Kurtz's real genius lay in politics. Can you develop on these notions? Of what importance is language to politics? What is its connection with power, especially (for Conrad clearly is speaking of politics in a disparaging way)? Have you read George Orwell on Newspeak in the "novel," *1984*?
8. Marlow also appears in Conrad's "Youth," *Lord Jim,* and *Chance.* (Conrad uses other narrators in other works, notably "Amy Foster" and *Under Western Eyes*). Read the "Marlow books," and write a paper characterizing Marlow more fully, tracing the changes in his nature. Discuss Conrad's use of him as a fictional device. In two he is the central character, but in *Chance* and *Lord Jim* he is not; what role does he play? Is he more effective than other Conradian narrators?
9. See pages 31, 43 of "Heart of Darkness." Is the Fool really safe? Is he fortunate? Is the Harlequin Russian an example of the Fool in "Heart of Darkness"? (By the way, how does his interest in Towson's book square with the rest of his portrayal?) With Jean-Aubry's comment (p. 100 above) on Conrad as a "mere animal" in mind, could you consider the Harlequin as Conrad's commentary on himself when young? Conrad has other categories of Man, but none of them are safe. In *Lord Jim,* the imaginative man's defects are drawn; in *Victory* the failures of both the sceptic (Heyst) and the foolish optimist (Morrison) are analyzed; in *Typhoon* the stolid man is very nearly extolled. Read these books and discuss the ways in which Marlow is superior (at the end of "Heart of Darkness") to all these types.
10. Conrad explicitly speaks of Marlow's adventure as a voyage. On page 5 we find Marlow saying, for instance, that "It was the farthest point of navigation and the culminating point of my experience." Discuss "Heart of Darkness" as an example of the journey or voyage as symbol.
11. Interesting comparisons of "Heart of Darkness" to other works can be made. For example, compare and contrast Graham Greene's *The Heart of the Matter,* which by its very title is a graceful acknowledgment of the novelist's indebtedness to Conrad.
12. Why is Marlow rude to the people in the sepulchral city when he returns to Europe? Why is it he says his imagination wanted soothing (p. 64)? How does his Lie apply here?

    From this issue many interesting comparisons can be made. Read *Gulliver's Travels* by Jonathan Swift. Contrast the last part with the end of "Heart of Darkness." After Gulliver has compared the Houyhnhnms with the Yahoos, and returned to his home, he is unable to accept life. The sight of his wife and family "filled me only with hatred, disgust, and contempt." Contrast Conrad's solution to Marlow's related problem. Which is the richer interpretation of life?

Or, read Nathaniel Hawthorne's short story, "Young Goodman Brown." After Brown has gone into the forest and seen more deeply into general human nature (or specifically his own character, as the story may also be interpreted), he returns home but "shrank from the bosom" of his wife, Faith. "His dying hour was gloom." Again, contrast the central characters of the two stories, and discuss whether Conrad's or Hawthorne's interpretation of life is the richer.